IEEE Std 142-1991

(Revision of IEEE Std 142-1982)

IEEE Recommended Practice for Grounding of Industrial and Commercial Power Systems

Sponsor
Power Systems Engineering Committee
of the
IEEE Industry Applications Society

Approved June 27, 1991
IEEE Standards Board

Approved December 9, 1991
American National Standards Institute

Abstract: The problems of system grounding, that is, connection to ground of neutral, of the corner of the delta, or of the midtap of one phase, are covered. The advantages and disadvantages of grounded versus ungrounded systems are discussed. Information is given on how to ground the system, where the system should be grounded, and how to select equipment for the grounding of the neutral circuits. Connecting the frames and enclosures of electric apparatus, such as motors, switchgear, transformers, buses, cables conduits, building frames, and portable equipment, to a ground system is addressed. The fundamentals of making the interconnection or ground-conductor system between electric equipment and the ground rods, water pipes, etc. are outlined. The problems of static electricity—how it is generated, what processes may produce it, how it is measured, and what should be done to prevent its generation or to drain the static charges to earth to prevent sparking—are treated. Methods of protecting structures against the effects of lightning are also covered. Obtaining a low-resistance connection to the earth, use of ground rods, connections to water pipes, etc. is discussed. A separate chapter on sensitive electronic equipment is included.
Keywords: System grounding, equipment grounding, static and lightning protection grounding, connection to earth, and sensitive electronic equipment grounding.

Corrected Edition

Third Printing

April 1996

This edition incorporates corrections to minor typographical errors. In several cases, typographical errors in the original text could lead to misinterpretation. Changes of this type are indicated in the text by a change bar running in the left margin next to the corrected line in the text. This occurs on pages 25, 26, 31, 85, 137, 176, 180, and 181.

The Institute of Electrical and Electronics Engineers, Inc.

345 East 47th Street, New York NY 10017-2394, USA

Copyright © 1992 by the

Institute of Electrical and Electronics Engineers, Inc.

All rights reserved. Published 1992

Printed in the United States of America

ISBN 1-55937-141-2

Library of Congress Catalog Card Number 92-81909

June 22, 1992

SH14498

IEEE Standards documents are developed within the Technical Committees of the IEEE Societies and the Standards Coordinating Committees of the IEEE Standards Board. Members of the committees serve voluntarily and without compensation. They are not necessarily members of the Institute. The standards developed within IEEE represent a consensus of the broad expertise on the subject within the Institute as well as those activities outside of IEEE which have expressed an interest in participating in the development of the standard.

Use of an IEEE Standard is wholly voluntary. The existence of an IEEE Standard does not imply that there are no other ways to produce, test, measure, purchase, market, or provide other goods and services related to the scope of the IEEE Standard. Furthermore, the viewpoint expressed at the time a standard is approved and issued is subject to change brought about through developments in the state of the art and comments received from users of the standard. Every IEEE Standard is subjected to review at least every five years for revision or reaffirmation. When a document is more than five years old, and has not been reaffirmed, it is reasonable to conclude that its contents, although still of some value, do not wholly reflect the present state of the art. Users are cautioned to check to determine that they have the latest edition of any IEEE Standard.

Comments for revision of IEEE Standards are welcome from any interested party, regardless of membership affiliation with IEEE. Suggestions for changes in documents should be in the form of a proposed change of text, together with appropriate supporting comments.

Interpretations: Occasionally questions may arise regarding the meaning of portions of standards as they relate to specific applications. When the need for interpretations is brought to the attention of IEEE, the Institute will initiate action to prepare appropriate responses. Since IEEE Standards represent a consensus of all concerned interests, it is important to ensure that any interpretation has also received the concurrence of a balance of interests. For this reason IEEE and the members of its technical committees are not able to provide an instant response to interpretation requests except in those cases where the matter has previously received formal consideration.

Comments on standards and requests for interpretations should be addressed to:

> Secretary, IEEE Standards Board
> 445 Hoes Lane
> P.O. Box 1331
> Piscataway, NJ 08555-1331
> USA

Foreword

(This Foreword is not a part of IEEE Std 142-1991, IEEE Recommended Practice for Grounding of Industrial and Commercial Power Systems.)

This book is a revision of IEEE Std 142-1982. This recommended practice has served electrical engineers seeking electrical system grounding information since the first edition in 1956. It reflects the experience and sound judgment of a working group made up of engineers active in the design and operation of electrical systems for industrial and commercial power systems.

The working group owes a debt of gratitude to the authors of previous editions. The members of the working group for the original 1956 edition were: D. L. Beeman (Chairman), D. M. Allison, H. H. Angel, J. E. Arberry, K. M. Bausch, A. J. Bisson, L. J. Carpenter, M. A. Leland, F. R. Longley, C. C. Saunders, J. M. Schmidt, H. E. Springer, H. M. Stewart, T. O. Sweatt, H. B. Thacker, and B. F. Thomas, Jr. Others who worked on the interim editions that were not on the present working group are: Thad Brown, W. H. Cook, L. S. Corey, J. W. Couter, D. C. Grant, C. A. Hatstat, T. L. Haymes, C. F. Hedlund, R. H. Kaufmann, R. Loewe, B. K. Mathur, E. S. Raila, and F. J. Shields.

We consider this a major revision of the text. Much new material has become available since the 1982 edition. Chapter 1, System Grounding, has been expanded and revised throughout. Chapter 2, Equipment Grounding, has been carefully reviewed and revised in the light of experience. Chapter 3, Static and Lightning Protection Grounding, has important new material on grounding of high-rise structures. Chapter 4, Connection to Earth, required the fewest changes but has important updating, such as the caution in using stainless steel ground rods. Chapter 5, Sensitive Electronic Equipment Grounding, is completely new. It includes methods of grounding that include noise control and are consistent with the National Electrical Code.

This has been a project of the Power Systems Grounding Subcommittee of the Power Systems Engineering Committee. Members of the subcommittee and working group during this period were:

Gordon S. Johnson, *Chair*

Kenneth E. Almon	Daleep C. Mohla	Lynn F. Saunders
Baldwin Bridger	Richard L. Nailen	Robert L. Simpson
Newton S. Burley	William J. Neiswender	Mark G. Theriault
Edward Cantwell	Neil Nichols	S. I. Venugopalan
Ralph H. Lee (deceased)	Dev Paul	Donald W. Zipse
Richard E. Loyd	Elliot Rappaport	
Robert G. Medley	Milt Robinson	

The working group received invaluable comments and text material from coordinating groups in the Power Systems Protection Committee, the Computer Society, the Power Engineering Society, the National Electrical Manufacturers Association, Underwriters Laboratories, the International Electrotechnical Commission, and others. A partial list of other contributors and reviewers includes:

Carrol Burtner	Ches Heath	S. R. Mendis
Walter V. Chumakov	John Holladay	Lloyd A. Morley
Norman H. Davis, III	David Jackson	James Prothero
Robert Dempsey	Richard P. Keil	James Skiles
Paul Duks	Charles A. Lennon	
Thomas Gruz	Daniel Love	

The following persons were on the balloting committee that approved this document for submission to the IEEE Standards Board:

Kenneth E. Almon	Daleep C. Mohla	Milt Robinson
Baldwin Bridger	Richard L. Nailen	Lynn F. Saunders
Newton S. Burley	William J. Neiswender	Robert L. Simpson
Edward Cantwell	Neil Nichols	Mark G. Theriault
Gordon S. Johnson	Dev Paul	S. I. Venugopalan
Robert G. Medley	Elliot Rappaport	Donald W. Zipse

When the IEEE Standards Board approved this standard on June 27, 1991, it had the following membership:

IEEE Recommended Practice for Grounding of Industrial and Commercial Power Systems

5th Edition

Working Group Members and Contributors

Gordon Johnson, *Working Group Chair*

Chapter 1—System Grounding:

Neil Nichols, *Chair*

Chapter 2—Equipment Grounding:

Elliot Rappaport, *Chair*

Chapter 3—Static and Lightning Protection Grounding:

Baldwin Bridger, *Chair*

Chapter 4—Connection to Earth:

Kenneth B. Almon, *Chair*

Chapter 5—Sensitive Electronic Equipment Grounding:

Donald W. Zipse and Ralph H. Lee, *Cochairs*

IEEE Recommended Practice for Grounding of Industrial and Commercial Power Systems

Chapter 1

System Grounding

1.1 Introduction

Grounding of an electrical system is a decision that must be faced sometime by most engineers charged with planning or modifying electrical distribution. Grounding in some form is generally recommended, although there are certain exceptions. Several methods and criteria exist for system grounding; each has its own purpose.

It is the intention of this section to assist the engineer in making decisions on the subject by presenting basic reasons for grounding or not grounding and by reviewing general practices and methods of system grounding.

The practices set forth herein are primarily applicable to industrial power systems that distribute and utilize power at medium or low voltage, usually within a smaller geographical area than is covered by a utility.

Where distances or power levels may dictate circuitry and equipment similar to a utility, consideration of utility practices is warranted. However, restrictions of the National Electrical Code (NEC) (ANSI/NFPA 70–1990) [1],[1] particular needs of service, and the experience and training of the workforce should also be considered.

Where an industrial power system includes power-generating equipment, the reasons for grounding these components may be the same as those for grounding similar components of public utility systems. The methods of grounding would generally be similar under like conditions of service. However, in the industrial setting, conditions of service may be altered by:

1) Location within the power system
2) Individual generator characteristics
3) Manufacturing process requirements

---

[1]The numbers in brackets correspond to those of the references in 1.12.

All of these may affect grounding decisions.

The NEC [1], sponsored by the National Fire Protection Association, contains regulations pertaining to system and equipment grounding applicable to industrial, commercial, and special occupancy facilities. These rules are considered minimum requirements for the protection of life and property and should be carefully reviewed during the course of system design.

1.2 Definitions

The varieties of system grounding and definitions of related terminology follow. The definitions of additional terms may be found in IEEE Std 100-1988 [2] and the NEC [1].

effectively grounded: Grounded through a sufficiently low impedance such that for all system conditions the ratio of zero-sequence reactance to positive-sequence reactance (X_0/X_1) is positive and less than 3, and the ratio of zero-sequence resistance to positive-sequence reactance (R_0/X_1) is positive and less than 1.

grounded system: A system in which at least one conductor or point (usually the middle wire or neutral point of transformer or generator windings) is intentionally grounded, either solidly or through an impedance.

grounded: Connected to earth or to some extended conducting body that serves instead of the earth, whether the connection is intentional or accidental.

high resistance grounded: A grounded system with a purposely inserted resistance that limits ground-fault current such that the current can flow for an extended period without exacerbating damage. This level of current is commonly thought to be 10 A or less. High-resistance grounded systems are designed to meet the criterion of $R_0 \leq X_{CO}$ to limit the transient overvoltages due to arcing ground faults. X_{CO} is the distributed per-phase capacitive reactance to ground of the system, and R_O is the per-phase zero-sequence resistance of the system.

low resistance grounded: A resistance-grounded system in which the purposely inserted resistance has lower ohmic value than would meet the high-resistance grounding criteria. The resistance is selected to provide the desired relaying current.

per-phase charging current: (I_{CO}). The current (V_{LN}/X_{CO}) that passes through one phase of the system to charge the distributed capacitance per phase to ground of the system, V_{L-N} is the line-to-neutral voltage and X_{CO} is the per-phase distributed capacitive reactance of the system.

R_0: The per-phase zero-sequence resistance of the system.

reactance grounded: Grounded through impedance, the principal element of which is inductive reactance.

resistance grounded: Grounded through an impedance, the principal element of which is resistance.

resonance: The enhancement of the response of a physical system (electrical system or circuit) to a periodic excitation when the excitation frequency (f) is equal to a natural frequency of the system. In a series circuit consisting of resistance (R), inductance (L), and capacitance (C), when L and C parameters are such that the resultant reactance becomes zero and the current reaches maximum, then the circuit is in series resonance. This happens when

$$\omega L = \frac{1}{\omega C} \text{ or } f = \frac{1}{2\pi\sqrt{LC}}$$

Similarly, in a parallel circuit consisting of R, L, and C, the admittance is the lowest when $1/X_1 = 1/X_c$, and the circuit is in parallel resonance. This happens when

$$\omega L = \frac{1}{\omega C} \text{ or } f = \frac{1}{2\pi\sqrt{LC}}$$

R_n: The value of the resistance connected from the neutral to the ground of a resistance-grounded system. For high-resistance grounded systems where R_N is a major component of R_o, the relationship $R_0 = 3R_N$ applies.

solidly grounded: Connected directly through an adequate ground connection in which no impedance has been intentionally inserted.

static charge: The electricity generated when two dissimilar substances come into contact. Conveyor belts are active producers of static electricity.

switching surge: A transient wave of overvoltage in an electric circuit caused by the operation of a switching device interrupting load current or fault current.

system: A grounding system consists of all interconnected grounding connections in a specific power system and is defined by its isolation from adjacent; grounding systems. The isolation is provided by transformer primary and secondary windings that are coupled only by magnetic means. Thus, the system boundary is defined by the lack of a physical connection that is either metallic or through a significantly high impedance. Fig 1 illustrates the limits and boundaries of grounding systems.

system charging current: The total distributed capacitive charging current ($3V_{LN}/X_{CO}$) of a three-phase system.

three-phase four-wire system: A system of alternating current supply comprising four conductors, three of which are connected as in a three-phase three-wire system, the fourth being connected to the neutral point of the supply or midpoint of one-phase in case of delta-connected transformer secondary, which may be grounded.

three-phase three-wire system: A system of alternating current supply comprising three conductors, between successive pairs of which are maintained alternating differences of potential successively displaced in phase by one third of a period.

transient overvoltage: The temporary overvoltage of short duration associated with the operation of the switching device, a fault, a lightning stroke, or during arcing ground faults on the ungrounded system.

ungrounded system: A system, without an intentional connection to ground, except through potential indicating or measuring devices or other very high impedance devices.

1.3 Purposes of System Grounding

System grounding, or the intentional connection of a phase or neutral conductor to earth, is for the purpose of controlling the voltage to earth, or ground, within predictable limits. It also provides for a flow of current that will allow detection of an unwanted connection between system conductors and ground and which may instigate operation of automatic devices to remove the source of voltage from conductors with such undesired connections to ground. The NEC [1], prescribes certain system grounding connections that must be made to be in compliance with the code. The control of voltage to ground limits the voltage stress on the insulation of conductors so that insulation performance can more readily be predicted. The control of voltage also allows reduction of shock hazard to persons who might come in contact with live conductors.

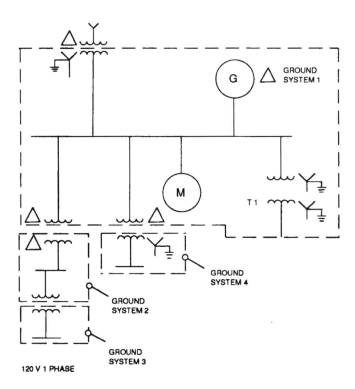

Figure 1—Grounding Systems

1.4 Methods of System Neutral Grounding

1.4.1 Introduction

Most grounded systems employ some method of grounding the system neutral at one or more points. These methods can be divided into two general categories: Solid grounding and impedance grounding. Impedance grounding may be further divided into several subcategories: Reactance grounding, resistance grounding and ground-fault-neutralizer grounding. Fig 2 shows examples of these methods of grounding. Each method, as named, refers to the nature of the external circuit from system neutral to ground rather than to the degree of grounding. In each case the impedance of the generator or transformer whose neutral is grounded is in series with the external circuit. Thus a solidly grounded generator or transformer may or may not furnish effective grounding to the system, depending on the system source impedance.

Many of the concepts involved in defining system-grounding types and levels are best explained in terms of symmetrical components or equivalent circuits. The reader who is not familiar with these analytical methods is referred to Chapter 2 of Beeman [10] and to Chapter 3 of the *IEEE Brown Book* [5] for guidance.

Molded-case circuit-breaker interrupting capabilities can be affected by the method of grounding. If other than effective grounding is used, circuit breakers should be reevaluated for the application.

1.4.2 Ungrounded Systems (No Intentional Grounding)

Electrical power systems which are operated with no intentional ground connection to the system conductors are generally described as ungrounded. In reality, these systems are grounded through the system capacitance to ground.

In most systems, this is an extremely high impedance, and the resulting system relationships to ground are weak and easily distorted.

Two principal advantages are attributed to ungrounded systems. The first is operational: The first ground fault on a system causes only a small ground current to flow, so the system may be operated with a ground fault present, improving system continuity. The second is economic: No expenditures are required for grounding equipment or grounded system conductors.

Numerous advantages are attributed to grounded systems, including greater safety, freedom from excessive system overvoltages that can occur on ungrounded systems during arcing, resonant or near-resonant ground faults, and easier detection and location of ground faults when they do occur.

Resonant effects can occur when the ground fault path includes an inductive reactance approximately equal to the system capacitive reactance to ground. Beeman [10], pp. 281–285, discusses this phenomenon in depth. For an extensive discussion of the advantages of grounded systems, see pp 345–348 of Beeman [10]. Also, Article 250–5 of [1] requires certain systems to be grounded. Grounded systems are now the predominant choice.

When an ungrounded system is chosen, a ground detection scheme may be applied to the system. This scheme frequently takes the form of three voltage transformers with their primary windings connected in wye and with the primary neutral grounded. The secondary windings of the voltage transformers are usually connected in broken delta, with a voltage relay connected in the open corner and used to operate an indication or alarm circuit. Loading resistors may be required either in the primary neutral circuit or in the secondary circuit to avoid ferroresonance.

1.4.3 Resistance Grounding

In resistance grounding, the neutral is connected to ground through one or more resistors. In this method, with the resistor values normally used, and except for transient overvoltages, the line-to-ground voltages that exist during a line-to-ground fault are nearly the same as those for an ungrounded system.

A system properly grounded by resistance is not subject to destructive transient overvoltages. For resistance-grounded systems at 15 kV and below, such overvoltages will not ordinarily be of a serious nature if the resistance value lies within the following boundary limits: $R_0 \le X_{C0}$, $R_0 \ge 2X_0$. The corresponding ground-fault current is far less than is normally used for low-resistance grounding, but is the design criterion for high-resistance grounding.

The reasons for limiting the current by resistance grounding may be one or more of the following.

1) To reduce burning and melting effects in faulted electric equipment, such as switchgear, transformers, cables, and rotating machines.
2) To reduce mechanical stresses in circuits and apparatus carrying fault currents.
3) To reduce electric-shock hazards to personnel caused by stray ground-fault currents in the ground return path.
4) To reduce the arc blast or flash hazard to personnel who may have accidentally caused or who happen to be in close proximity to the ground fault.
5) To reduce the momentary line-voltage dip occasioned by the occurrence and clearing of a ground fault.
6) To secure control of transient overvoltages while at the same time avoiding the shutdown of a faulty circuit on the occurrence of the first ground fault (high-resistance grounding).

Resistance grounding may be either of two classes, high resistance or low resistance, distinguished by the magnitude of ground-fault current permitted to flow. Although there are no recognized standards for the levels of ground-fault current that define these two classes, in practice there is a clear difference. High-resistance grounding typically uses ground-fault current levels of 10 A or less, although some specialized systems at voltages in the 15 kV class may have higher ground-fault current levels. Low-resistance grounding typically uses ground-fault current levels of at least 100 A, with currents in the 200–1000 A range being more usual.

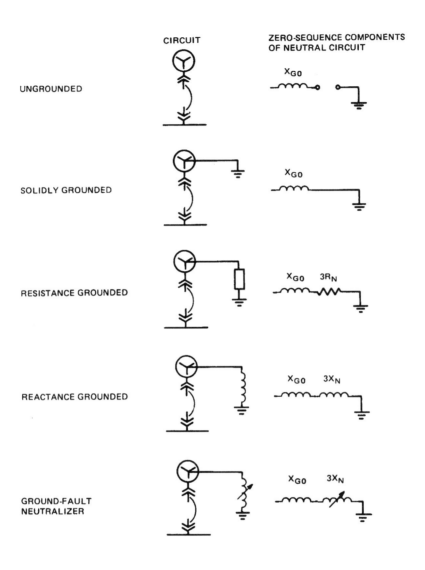

X_{GO} = Zero-sequence reactance of generator or transformer
X_N = Reactance of grounding reactor
R_N = Resistance of grounding resistor

Figure 2—System Neutral Circuit and Equivalent Diagrams for Ungrounded and Various Types of Grounded-Neutral Systems

Both types are designed to limit transient overvoltages to a safe level (within 250% of normal). However, the high-resistance method usually does not require immediate clearing of a ground fault since the fault current is limited to a very low level. This low level must be at least equal to the system total capacitance-to-ground charging current. The protective scheme associated with high-resistance grounding is usually detection and alarm rather than immediate tripout. In general the use of high-resistance grounding on systems where the line-to-ground fault current exceeds 10 A should be avoided because of the damage potential of an arcing current larger than 10 A in a confined space.

The low-resistance method has the advantage of immediate and selective clearing of the grounded circuit, but requires that the minimum ground-fault current be large enough to positively actuate the applied ground-fault relay. High-resistance grounding is a method that can be applied to existing medium-voltage ungrounded systems to obtain the transient overvoltage protection without the modification expense of adding ground relays to each circuit.

Systems grounded through resistors require surge arresters suitable for use on ungrounded-neutral circuits. Metal oxide surge arrester ratings must be chosen so that neither the maximum continuous operating voltage capability nor the one-second temporary overvoltage capability is exceeded under system ground fault conditions.

1.4.4 Reactance Grounding

The term *reactance grounding* describes the case in which a reactor is connected between the system neutral and ground. Since the ground-fault that may flow in a reactance-grounded system is a function of the neutral reactance, the magnitude of the ground-fault current is often used as a criterion for describing the degree of grounding. In a reactance-grounded system, the available ground-fault current should be at least 25% and preferably 60% of the three-phase fault current to prevent serious transient overvoltages ($X_0 \leq 10X_1$). This is considerably higher than the level of fault current desirable in a resistance-grounded system, and therefore reactance grounding is usually not considered an alternative to resistance grounding.

In most generators, solid grounding, that is, grounding without external impedance, may permit the maximum ground-fault current from the generator to exceed the maximum three-phase fault current that the generator can deliver and for which its windings are braced. Consequently, neutral-grounded generators should be grounded through a low-value reactor that will limit the ground-fault current to a value no greater than the generator three-phase fault current. In the case of three-phase four-wire systems, the limitation of ground-fault current to 100% of the three-phase fault current is usually practical without interfering with normal four-wire operation. In practice, reactance grounding is generally used only in this case and to ground substation transformers with similar characteristics.

1.4.5 Ground-Fault Neutralizer (Resonant Grounding)

A ground-fault neutralizer is a reactor connected between the neutral of a system and ground and having a specially selected, relatively high value of reactance. The reactance is tuned to the system charging current so that the resulting ground fault current is resistive and of a low magnitude. This current is in phase with the line-to-neutral voltage, so that current zero and voltage zero occur simultaneously. If the ground fault is in air, such as an insulator flashover, it may be self-extinguishing. This method of grounding is used primarily on systems above 15 kV, consisting largely of overhead transmission or distribution lines. Since systems of such construction are rarely used in industrial or commercial power systems, the ground-fault neutralizer finds little application in these systems. For further information on the use of ground-fault neutralizers, see Reference [9].

1.4.6 Solid Grounding

Solid grounding refers to the connection of the neutral of a generator, power transformer, or grounding transformer directly to the station ground or to the earth.

Because of the reactance of the grounded generator or transformer in series with the neutral circuit, a solid ground connection does not provide a zero-impedance neutral circuit. If the reactance of the system zero-sequence circuit is too great with respect to the system positive-sequence reactance, the objectives sought in grounding, principally freedom from transient overvoltages, may not be achieved. This is rarely a problem in typical industrial and commercial power systems. The zero-sequence impedance of most generators used in these systems is much lower than the positive-sequence impedance of these generators. The zero-sequence impedance of a delta-wye transformer will not exceed the transformer's positive-sequence impedance. There are, however, conditions under which relatively high zero-sequence impedance may occur.

One of these conditions is a power system fed by several generators and/or transformers in parallel. If the neutral of only one source is grounded, it is possible for the zero-sequence impedance of the grounded source to exceed the effective positive-sequence impedance of the several sources in parallel.

Another such condition may occur where power is distributed to remote facilities by an overhead line without a metallic ground return path. In this case, the return path for ground-fault current is through the earth, and, even though both the neutral of the source and the nonconducting parts at the load may be grounded with well-made electrodes, the ground return path includes the impedance of both of these ground electrodes. This impedance may be significant. Another significant source of zero sequence impedance is the large line-to-ground spacing of the overhead line.

To ensure the benefits of solid grounding, it is necessary to determine the degree of grounding provided in the system. A good guide in answering this question is the magnitude of ground-fault current as compared to the system three-phase fault current. The higher the ground-fault current in relation to the three-phase fault current the greater the degree of grounding in the system. Effectively grounded systems will have a line-to-ground short circuit current of at least 60% of the three-phase short-circuit value. In terms of resistance and reactance, effective grounding of a system is accomplished only when $R_0 \leq X_1$ and $X_0 \leq 3X_1$ and such relationships exist at any point in the system. The X_1 component used in the above relation is the Thevenin equivalent positive-sequence reactance of the complete system including the subtransient reactance of all rotating machines.

Application of surge arresters for grounded-neutral service requires that the system be effectively grounded.

1.4.7 Obtaining the System Neutral

The best way to obtain the system neutral for grounding purposes in three-phase systems is to use source transformers or generators with wye-connected windings. The neutral is then readily available. Such transformers are available for practically all voltages except 240 V. On new systems, 208Y/120 V or 480Y/277 V wye-connected transformers may be used to good advantage instead of 240 V. Wye-connected source transformers for 2400, 4160, and 13 800 V systems are available as a standard option, whereas 4800 and 6900 V wye-connected source transformers may be priced at a premium rate. The alternative is to apply grounding transformers.

System neutrals may not be available, particularly in many old systems of 600 V or less and many existing 2400, 4800, and 6900 V systems. When existing delta-connected systems are to be grounded, grounding transformers may be used to obtain the neutral. Grounding transformers may be of either the zigzag, the wye-delta, or the T-connected type. One type of grounding transformer commonly used is a three-phase zigzag transformer with no secondary winding. The internal connection of the transformer is illustrated in Fig 3. The impedance of the transformer to balanced three-phase voltages is high so that when there is no fault on the system, only a small magnetizing current flows in the transformer winding. The transformer impedance to zero-sequence voltages, however, is low so that it allows high ground-fault currents to flow. The transformer divides the ground-fault current into three equal components; these currents are in phase with each other and flow in the three windings of the grounding transformer. The method of winding is seen from Fig 3 to be such that when these three equal currents flow, the current in one section of the winding of each leg of the core is in a direction opposite to that in the other section of the winding on that leg. This tends to force the ground-fault current to have equal division in the three lines and accounts for the low impedance of the transformer-to-ground currents.

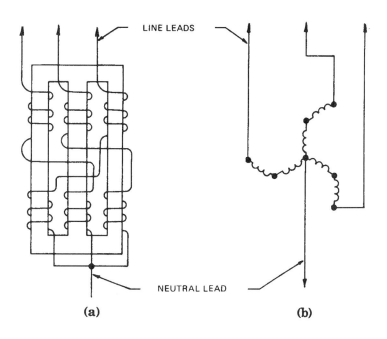

**Figure 3—(a) Core Windings
(b) Connections of Three-Phase Zigzag Grounding Transformer**

A wye-delta-connected three-phase transformer or transformer bank can also be utilized for system grounding. As in the case of the zigzag grounding transformer, the usual application is to accomplish resistance-type grounding of an existing ungrounded system. The delta connection must be closed to provide a path for the zero-sequence current, and the delta voltage rating is selected for any standard value. A resistor inserted between the primary neutral and ground, as shown in Fig 4, provides a means for limiting ground-fault current to a level satisfying the criteria for resistance-grounded systems. For this arrangement, the voltage rating of the wye winding need not be greater than the normal line-to-neutral system voltage. For high-resistance grounding it is sometimes more practical or economical to apply the limiting resistor in the secondary delta connection. Three single-phase distribution class transformers are used, with the primary wye neutral connected directly to ground. The secondary delta is closed through a resistor that effectively limits the primary ground-fault current to the desired low level. For this alternative application, the voltage rating of each of the transformer windings forming the wye primary should not be less than the system line-to-line voltage.

The rating of a three-phase grounding transformer or bank, in kVA, is equal to the rated line-to-neutral voltage in kilovolts times the rated neutral current [18]. Most grounding transformers are designed to carry their rated current for a limited time only, such as 10 s or 1 min. Consequently, they are much smaller in size than an ordinary three-phase continuously rated transformer with the same rating.

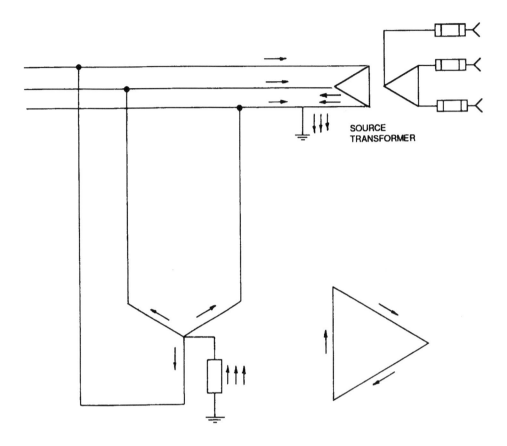

Figure 4—Vectors Representing Current Flow in Wye-Delta Transformer Used as Grounding Transformer with Line-to Ground Fault

It is generally desirable to connect a grounding transformer directly to the main bus of a power system, without intervening circuit breakers or fuses, to prevent the transformer from being inadvertently taken out of service by the operation of the intervening devices. (In this case the transformer is considered part of the bus and is protected by the relaying applied for bus protection.) Alternatively, the grounding transformer should be served by a dedicated feeder circuit breaker, as shown in Fig 5(a), or connected between the main transformer and the main switchgear, as illustrated in Fig 5(b). If the grounding transformer is connected as shown in Fig 5(b), there should be one grounding transformer for each delta-connected bank supplying power to the system, or enough grounding transformers to assure at least one grounding transformer on the system at all times. When the grounding transformer is so connected, it is included in the protective system of the main transformer.

1.5 Grounding at Points Other than System Neutral

In some cases, low-voltage systems (600 V and below) are grounded at some point other than the system neutral to obtain a grounded electrical system. This is done where exiting delta transformer connections do not provide access to the system neutral. Two systems are in general use.

1.5.1 Corner-of-the-Delta Systems

Low-voltage systems, which in the past have been nearly all supplied from transformers with delta-connected secondaries, have been ungrounded. Grounding of one-phase corner-of-the-delta grounding has sometimes been used as a means of obtaining a grounded system. The advantages are the following:

1) It is the least costly method of converting an ungrounded delta system to a grounded system. This method was adapted by one very large industrial company in 1935 for their older plants. No problems have been reported and it is still in use. The first costs of a new transformer are approximately the same for either a delta or a wye secondary connection.
2) Although motor overload protection, theoretically, is needed only in the two phases that are not grounded, the NEC Table 430–37 states that for three-phase systems, three overloads are required, one in each phase. The advantage in the past of having only two overloads is no longer viable.
3) With properly connected control circuits, ground faults in the control circuit will neither start the motor nor prevent stopping the motor by means of the stop push button.
4) There is a high probability of sustaining arcing for 480 V or higher, phase-to-phase, single-phase circuit extension, without escalation to a three-phase fault.
5) The corner-grounded system will effectively control transient and overvoltages; however, a maximum of 1.73 times the normal phase-to-neutral voltage can exist between two conductors and the ground.
6) A fault from phase to ground is easily detected and found.

The disadvantages are the following:

1) An inability to supply dual-voltage service for lighting and power loads.
2) The necessity of positive identification of the grounded phase throughout the system to avoid connecting meters, fuses, instruments, and relays in the grounded phase.
3) A higher line-to-ground voltage on two phases than in a neutral-grounded system.
4) The possibility of exceeding interrupting capabilities of marginally applied circuit breakers, because for a ground fault, the interrupting duty on the affected circuit-breaker pole exceeds the three-phase fault duty.

Because of its limitations, this type of grounding has not been widely used in industrial systems.

1.5.2 One Phase of a Delta System Grounded at Midpoint

In some areas where the utility had a large single-phase 120/240 V load and a small three-phase 240 V load, they have supplied a large single-phase 120/240 transformer and one or two smaller 240 V transformers. In other cases where three single-phase transformers are connected in delta, the midpoint, if available, is grounded. With this method it is possible to gain some of the advantages of neutral grounding by grounding the midpoint of one phase. This method does not provide all the advantages of a system neutral grounding and is not recommended for voltages over 240 V. The advantages are the following:

1) The first costs are approximately the same as a solidly grounded system.
2) Fast tripping for phase-to-ground faults.
3) Mid-phase grounding effectively controls, to safe levels, the over-voltages.

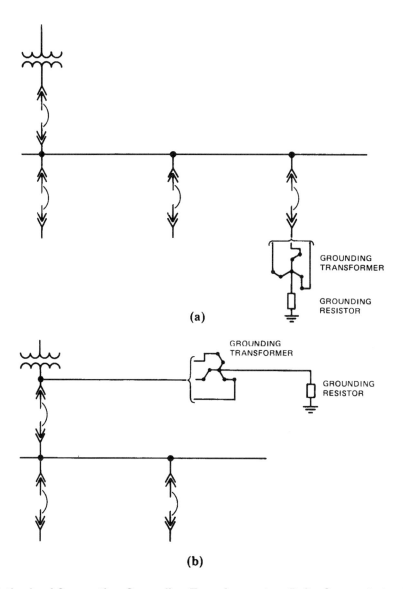

Figure 5—Methods of Connecting Grounding Transformer to a Delta-Connected or Ungrounded Power System to Form Neutral for System Grounding

The disadvantages are the following:

1) The shock hazard of the high phase leg to ground is 1.73 times the voltage from the other two phases.
2) There must be positive identification of the conductor with the highest voltage to ground to avoid connecting 120 V loads to that conductor.
3) Serious flash hazard from a phase-to-ground fault can exist because of the high fault levels.
4) The cost of maintenance is somewhat above the neutral grounded system due to the sustained higher voltage and insulation stress on one phase.
5) Grounding of one phase of a delta system at the midpoint of that phase for three-phase systems with phase-to-phase voltages over 240 V has little application.

1.6 Location of System Grounding Points

1.6.1 Selection

Each system as described in 1.2 of this chapter is defined by "its isolation from adjacent grounding systems. The isolation is provided by transformer primary and secondary windings." The new system created by each transformer or generator requires the establishment of a new system ground.

The selection of a system grounding point is influenced by whether the transformer or generator windings are connected "wye" or "delta" "Delta-wye" or "wye-delta" transformers effectively block the flow of zero-sequence current between systems. Although the wye connection is generally more conducive to system grounding because of the availability of a neutral connection, that fact alone should not be the sole criteria for the location of the system ground point.

The system ground point should always be at the power source. An archaic concept of grounding at the load or at other points in the system because of the availability of a convenient grounding point is not recommended because of the problems caused by multiple ground paths and because of the danger that the system could be left ungrounded and therefore unsafe. The National Electrical Code recognizes this danger and prohibits system grounding at any place except the source and/or service equipment.

As previously described in 1.4.6 of this chapter, grounding of other than neutrals may be accomplished with the use of zigzag grounding transformers or grounded wye primary-delta secondary grounding transformer banks connected directly to the phase bus.

1.6.2 Single Power Source

When a system has only one source of power (generator or transformer), grounding may be accomplished by connecting the source neutral to earth either directly or through a neutral impedance (Fig 6). Provision of a switch or circuit breaker to open the neutral circuit is not recommended. It is not desirable to operate the system ungrounded by having the ground connection open while the generator or transformer is in service.

In the event that some means of disconnecting the ground connection is required for measurement, testing, or repair, a disconnecting link should be used and only opened when the system is de-energized.

1.6.3 Multiple Power Sources

For installation with multiple power sources (i.e., generators or power transformers) interconnected that are or can be operated in parallel, the system ground can be accomplished in one of two ways:

1) Each source grounded, with or without impedance (Fig 7).
2) Each source neutral connected to a common neutral bus, which is the grounded, with or without impedance (Fig 8).

For Solidly Grounded Systems with multiple sources where all sources must be solidly grounded, it is always acceptable to separately ground each power source as shown in Fig 7(a). Levels of fault current are determined by the number and available fault current of each interconnected source. Where sources are in close proximity, Common Ground Point connection [Fig 8(a) will allow for selective relaying to identify and isolate only the faulted source.

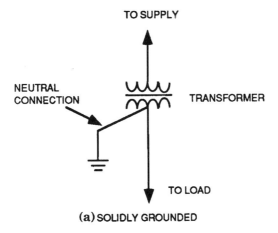

(a) SOLIDLY GROUNDED

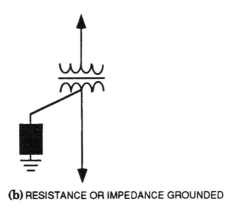

(b) RESISTANCE OR IMPEDANCE GROUNDED

Figure 6—Grounding for Systems with One Source of Power

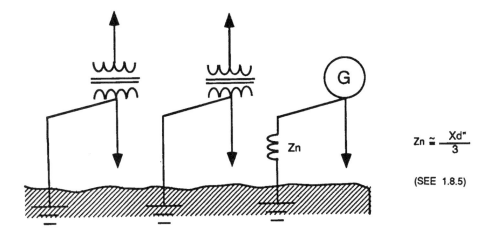

$$Zn \simeq \frac{Xd''}{3}$$

(SEE 1.8.5)

(a) SOLIDLY GROUNDED

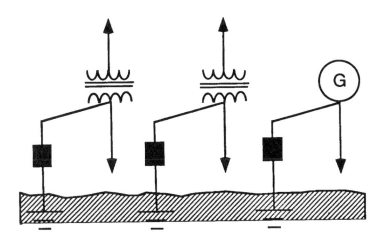

(b) R OR Z GROUNDED

**Figure 7—Grounding for Systems with Multiple Power Sources
(Method 1)**

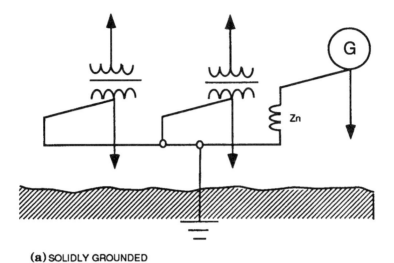

(a) SOLIDLY GROUNDED

NOTE: Procedure required
to prevent Switching Neutral
under load.

(b) R OR Z GROUNDED WITH NEUTRAL SWITCHING

**Figure 8—Grounding for Systems with Multiple Power Sources
(Method 2)**

If the power sources are not in close proximity, Common Ground Point is not recommended. The impedance in the neutral bus connection may become large enough to prevent effectively grounding the neutral of the source at the remote location. The interconnect may inadvertently become open, allowing the transformer to operate ungrounded.

For Impedance Grounded Systems it is always acceptable to separately connect each neutral to ground through individual impedances [Fig 7(b)]. Each impedance rating should allow sufficient current to satisfy the criteria for the grounding system being used.

Individual neutral switching devices (automatic or manual) are not recommended, since incorrect operation may allow a power source to operate ungrounded.

System relaying is more complex when such impedance grounding is used, because of multiple grounding points. Capability of detecting a ground fault at any point in the system requires sensing at each ground point in addition to any normal feeder protection. The fault current sensed by the feeder is variable, depending on the number of sources that are grounded at the time of the fault.

When individual impedances are used, circulation of third-harmonic currents between paralleled generators is not a problem since the impedance limits the circulating current to negligible values. When total ground-fault currents with several individual impedances would exceed about 1000–4000 A, a Common Ground Point and single impedance to limit the fault current should be considered [Fig 8(b)]. The advantage of this connection is that the maximum fault current is known and selective relaying can be used to open tie breakers and selectively isolate the faulted bus.

The primary purpose of neutral disconnecting devices in impedance grounded systems is to isolate the generator or transformer neutral from the neutral bus when the source is taken out of service, because the neutral bus is energized during ground faults. A generator or transformer disconnected from the power bus, but with an unbroken connection of its neutral to a neutral bus, would have all of its terminals elevated with respect to ground during a ground fault. Disconnecting devices should be metal-enclosed and interlocked in such a manner as to prevent their operation except when the transformer primary and secondary switches or generator main and field circuit breakers are open.

In the case of multiple transformers, all neutral isolating devices may be normally closed because the presence of delta-connected windings (which are nearly always present on at least one side of each transformer) minimizes the circulation of harmonic current between transformers. Generators that are designed to suppress zero sequence harmonics, usually by the use of a two-thirds pitch winding, will have negligible circulating currents when operated in parallel; therefore, it is often found practical to operate these types of generators with the neutral disconnect device closed. This simplifies the operating procedure and increases assurance that the system will be grounded at all times, because interlocking methods can be used.

It is sometimes desirable to operate with only one generator neutral disconnecting device closed at a time to eliminate any circulating harmonic or zero-sequence currents. In addition, this method provides control over the maximum ground fault current and simplifies ground relaying. When the generator whose neutral is grounded is to be shut down, another generator is grounded by means of its neutral disconnecting device before the main and neutral disconnecting device of the first one are opened. This method has some inherent safety considerations that must be recognized and addressed in order to ensure continual safe operation. The procedures required to permit only one disconnecting device to be closed with multiple sources generally do not permit the use of conventional interlocking methods to ensure that at least one neutral disconnecting device will be closed. Therefore, this method should only be used where strict supervision of operating procedures is assured.

When only one source is involved, but others are to be added to the station in the future, space should be allowed to add neutral switchgear when this becomes necessary.

1.6.4 Creation of Stray Currents and Potentials

If a current-carrying conductor, even though nominally at ground potential, is connected to earth at more than one location, part of the load current will flow through the earth because it is then in parallel with the grounded conductor. Since there is impedance in both the conductor and the earth, a voltage drop will occur both along the earth and the conductor. Most of the voltage drop in the earth will occur in the vicinity of the point of connection to earth, as explained in Chapter 4. Because of this nonlinear voltage drop in the earth, most of the earth will be at a different potential than the grounded conductor due to the load current flowing from this conductor to earth.

An equipment grounding conductor connected to the same electrode as the grounded load conductor will also have a potential difference from most of the earth due to the potential drop caused by the load current. In most instances the potential difference will be too low to present a shock hazard to persons or affect operation of conventional electrical load equipment. However, in many instances it has been of sufficient level to be detected by livestock, either by coming in contact with noncurrent carrying enclosures to which an equipment grounding conductor is connected, or where sufficient difference in potential exists between the earth contacts of the different hoofs. Although potential levels may not be life threatening to the livestock, it has been reported that as little as 0.5 V rms can affect milk production [17].

Section 250-24 of the NEC [1] has required that the grounded circuit conductor (neutral) of a single system must be connected to a different grounding electrode each time it enters a separate building. Where there is a multibuilding facility, as is common on farms, there will be load currents flowing in the earth due to these multiple groundings.

Section 250-24 has been modified by exceptions so that these multiple groundings are no longer universally required. Exception No. 2 will waive a neutral grounding at other than the service entrance from the utility if a separate equipment grounding conductor is run to each building and grounded and bonded at each building as specified in the code. Since no load current would be flowing into these grounding electrodes, the equipment grounding conductor should be at earth potential.

Another possible source of multigrounding of a neutral would be the use of the neutral for grounding of the frames of cooking ranges or clothes dryers as allowed in Article 250–61, Exception 1. If the appliance frame also has a separate connection to earth, the multigrounding of the neutral will be achieved. This practice should be avoided in the vicinity of the barns, and even at other locations on farms.

There is another condition of multigrounding, since the utility will ground the neutral at the supply transformer and it must be grounded again at the service entrance. Since the equipment grounding conductor has its origin at the service entrance ground, it will have a potential to earth as a function of the voltage drop created by load current in the earth in parallel with the service drop neutral current. The magnitude of this potential will be affected by the size and length of the service drop neutral, the magnitude of the neutral current, and the resistance to earth of the service entrance grounding electrode as well as other connections to earth of the equipment grounding conductor. These factors are all subject to some control.

It is recommended that sources of stray currents on the premises that can be created by grounding of the neutral at other than the service entrance should be eliminated. Do not ground the neutral except at the service entrance. Make regular checks of electrical circuits and equipment to assure that unintentional grounding of either line or neutral has not occurred due to insulation failures. It is also recommended that voltages caused by current in the service drop neutral be minimized by balancing loads to minimize neutral current. All loads creating irregular currents, such as motors, should not be connected line-to-neutral.

There is a remaining source of circulating current when the utility distribution circuit includes a multi-grounded neutral. The grounding of the supply-transformer secondary neutral has often been made common with the grounding of the primary neutral. It has been established that there may be a potential difference between this primary neutral and earth and that there may be primary load current flowing through the ground (see [26], [27], [24], and [17]). This will be affected by the neutral current, the location on the distribution feeder, and the effectiveness of the various ground electrodes.

Neutral-to-ground voltages injected into the user system from the utility primary neutral cannot be eliminated by system grounding techniques on the premises, although some reduction may be achieved if the service entrance ground is made extremely effective and is located at some distance from livestock facilities. There are active systems to counteract equipment-to-ground voltages produced by utility injections [17]. Also, used are so-called equipotential ground planes, which bring earth surface voltages to the same value as that of equipment [17]. Both of these are out of the scope of system grounding, but are mentioned for reader reference.

1.6.5 Grounding Locations Specified by the NEC [1]

The following are system locations of grounding connections that appear to be required or permitted for the more common power system groundings by the NEC [1]). This is not intended to be a complete listing of code requirements, and the current edition of the NEC should be consulted for details or recent changes as well as to determine whether grounding is required or prohibited. The purpose is to call attention to location requirements but not to interpret the requirements, since that is the province of the cognizant enforcing authorities.

On service-supplied systems of 50 to 1000 V, system grounding when required or elected should be made at the service entrance, between the load end of the service drop or lateral and the neutral landing point, and, if supplied from a transformer external to the building, also at one point external to the building. If a grounded conductor extends past the service entrance switch, it should have no further grounds on this extension except as noted by the various exceptions in the code to this requirement ([1], Sec. 250-23[a]), such as mentioned below.

Where dual services feed to a double-ended bus, a single ground at the center point of the neutral bus is allowed to replace those listed above ([1], Sec. 250-23[a], Exception 4).

If more than one building is fed from a single service there should be a system grounding connection made at the entrance to each building. However, if an equipment grounding conductor is run with the load conductors, this ground connection can be eliminated so as to avoid elevating noncurrent- carrying enclosures above ground potential due to load drop in the neutral conductor ([1], Sec. 250-23[a], Exception 2; Sec. 250-24[a], Exception 2; Sec. 547-8, Exception 1).

For circuits of 240 V or less, the code allows the grounded conductor to be used for grounding the frames of ranges, ovens, or clothes dryers ([1], Sec. 250-23[a], Exception 3). It does not prohibit simultaneous grounding by the equipment grounding conductor or to an effectively grounded water pipe, so that such connections could ground the neutral downstream of the service switch. This standard does not recommend that the grounded circuit conductor be connected to these appliance frames even if allowed by the code. It is recommended that the appliance frames be grounded by connection of an equipment grounding conductor.

Grounding connections should not be located or connected so as to cause objectionable currents in grounding conductors or grounding paths ([1], Sec. 250-21[a]).

Separately derived circuits, if required or elected to have a system ground, should be grounded between the source and the first disconnecting device. System grounding connections downstream of the disconnecting device have the same rules as for service-supplied circuits.

The point of grounding for systems shall be the neutral or common conductor where one exists, otherwise the point shall be a phase conductor ([1], Sec. 250-25).

On systems over 1000 V, a transformer-derived neutral may also be used as the attachment point for a system ground. This method is not mentioned for effective grounding of low-voltage systems.

High-voltage systems may also have multiple neutral grounds where the conductors are overhead outdoors, or where they are directly buried with a bare neutral conductor.

1.6.6 Avoiding Common-Mode Noise

When all of the conductors of a signal or power system have an identical potential difference with respect to another reference, this potential is known as a common-mode voltage or signal. If such voltage or signal is undesirable, it is usually called noise. The other references are usually the equipment enclosure or the ground, both of which may be at the same potential. Electronic equipment may often exhibit a susceptibility to common-mode noise between the incoming power conductors and ground, which may affect either digital or analog signals.

Common-mode noise on a power source occurs when a potential difference exists between the ground to which the power source is referenced and the ground to which the power-consuming equipment is referenced. There is often a capacitive or resistive coupling between the equipment's circuitry and its enclosure. The potential difference can be created when there is a current flow in the equipment grounding conductor, or the earth, between the equipment enclosure and the power source grounding.

The earth has many stray currents, resulting in small potential differences between points. These currents may be other than power frequencies, and even if power frequencies, may contain transients or bursts due to switching or other aberrations. Therefore, if the equipment cabinet is connected to earth at its location, any potential occurring between there and the power system grounding point can be coupled into the circuitry.

The equipment enclosure can be maintained at the same potential as the power system ground if the equipment grounding conductor is of low impedance and has no connection to earth except at the grounding point of the source transformer, the so-called "single point ground." This is allowed by the NEC 1], Sec. 250-74, Exception 4, and is referred to as an IG, or isolated ground outlet. Sec. 1.6.4 in this chapter illustrates why the neutral must be grounded only at the source transformer. The earth potential difference between the source grounding point and the equipment must not be sufficient to develop a shock hazard to persons standing within reach, and must not present the possibility of resistively or capacitively coupling this potential into the equipment enclosure at a magnitude sufficient to create a noise problem. Normally, meeting all these criteria is possible only if the equipment is physically and electrically close to the source transformer.

Connection of the equipment ground to earth with an electrode that is physically separate from all other power system and structural grounding electrodes and is not bonded to any of these other grounding electrodes, will inevitably produce common mode noise, since it is not referenced to the power source ground. The magnitude of this common mode potential can be destructive to the equipment and hazardous to personnel, since a power system fault can raise the power system or structure several hundred or thousand volts above other earth references. This grounding method is in violation of the NEC, Article 250 [1].

For greater detail on the grounding of sensitive equipment, refer to Chapter 5 of this standard and to P1100 [7].

1.6.7 Limiting Transferred Earth Potentials

The term *transferred earth potentials* refers to the voltage-to-earth of grounding systems that will appear on conductors as a result of the source system grounding electrode being above normal earth potential. The larger voltages are usually developed by ground fault currents returning to their source through earth. A common example is a ground fault of a conductor, which is supplying a substation transformer primary, to the station ground grid that is used for grounding of the transformer secondary neutral. If this grounding grid is not connected to the high-voltage source system ground, there can be a significant voltage rise above earth as the fault current flows into the earth. Low-voltage conductors leaving the area where the ground or grounding electrode voltage has been affected will have that voltage added to their normal line-to-ground voltage. The total voltage may exceed the insulating rating of the conductors or the equipment to which they are connected.

Control and telephone circuits running into areas where the grounding electrode or mat is subject to significant voltage rise are particularly vulnerable. High voltage appearing on such circuits is more likely to be a hazard to personnel and to exceed insulating ratings. Such conductors should not interconnect between two areas whose ground-mat potential is not held equal unless special protection or isolation is applied to the low voltage circuits. Another hazard can be created when portable or mobile equipment can be subjected to a transferred voltage rise. This is specifically treated in 1.11 as well as in Article 250–154 of the NEC [1].

Transferred potentials will be reduced if the resistance to earth or impedance between grounding grids is held to minimum. Isolation between low-voltage equipments at locations having unequal ground potentials can be accomplished by use of devices rejecting common-mode voltages. Such devices include isolation transformers, neutralizing reactors, or optical links [25].

Within most industrial distribution systems, compliance with the NEC requirements for equipment grounding conductors and the running of the grounding conductor to the service entrance panel serve to limit such potentials to safe limits. If there are areas that are interconnected by three-wire overhead lines only, bonding provisions should be made before interconnecting low-voltage circuits between the two areas.

Low-voltage potential differences can be created by the flow of load or other small currents through ground or grounding conductors. These can be quite troublesome to livestock, which is discussed in 1.6.4. It can also be troublesome to sensitive electronic equipment, particularly if the equipment is sensitive to common mode voltages on the power supply conductors or common-mode voltages on communication lines that may run between locations with different earth potentials. Existing NEC grounding requirements designed to prevent the flow of load currents through grounding paths are often not adequate because of the sensitivity to very low levels and because the voltages can be caused by other phenomena. These problems are further discussed in Chapter 5 and in P1100 [7].

Further information is available in Reference [25].

1.7 [Reserved for Future Use]

1.8 Grounding of Industrial Generators

1.8.1 Discussion of Generator Characteristics

Generators have several characteristics that are significantly different from transformers, the other common source of power. As compared to the transformer, the generator has little ability to withstand the heating effects or mechanical forces of short circuits. The generator may be required by standards to withstand a less than 10-per-unit short circuit, and the imposition of higher currents is defined as unusual service by the National Electrical Manufacturers Association (NEMA) M-G 1 [8], whereas a transformer may be required to withstand a 25-per-unit current. The generator may be capable of withstanding less than 25% of the heating effect of this current as compared to the transformer. If the current is unbalanced, this capability may be reduced to less than 10% of the transformer capability (see [8] and [23]).

Unlike the transformer, the three sequence reactances of a generator are not equal. The zero-sequence reactance has the lowest value, and the positive sequence reactance varies as a function of time. Thus, a generator will usually have higher initial ground-fault current than a three-phase fault current if the generator has a solidly grounded neutral. According to NEMA, the generator is required to withstand only the three-phase current level unless it is otherwise specified (see Reference 8). Also, NEMA states that the negative sequence current thermal withstand limit is a product of time in seconds and the square of per-unit negative sequence current (I_2^2t) equaling 40 [18]. With a solidly grounded neutral, the steady-state ground-fault current will be about eight times that of the full-load current when the steady-state three-phase fault current is three times the full-load current, but because of the negative sequence content of the ground-fault current, the generator has less thermal withstand capability than it would for a three-phase fault.

A generator can develop a significant third-harmonic voltage when loaded. A solidly grounded neutral and lack of external impedance to third harmonic current will allow flow of this third-harmonic current, whose value may approach rated current. If the winding is designed with a two-thirds pitch, this third-harmonic voltage will be suppressed [12] but the zero-sequence impedance will be lowered, increasing the ground-fault current.

The physical limitations imposed by generator construction result in less available insulation thicknesses, with a resulting reduction in voltage-impulse withstand as compared to nonrotating electrical equipment. Thus, special attention should be given to limiting voltage to ground by the grounding of generator neutrals.

Internal ground faults in solidly grounded generators can produce large fault currents. These currents can damage the laminated core, adding significantly to the time and cost of repair. Such currents persist until the generator voltage decays, since they are not capable of being interrupted by the generator circuit breaker [21]. Both magnitude and duration of these currents should be limited whenever possible.

NOTE — One per unit is equal to generator-rated current.

1.8.2 Single Unparalleled Generator

This configuration may offer the most options for grounding. The distribution system may be particularly designed for flexibility in applying grounding by having only three-wire loads connected directly to the generator or even having only a single transformer connected to the generator (unit bank). Thus the design may employ high-resistance grounding to minimize damage from internal ground faults, or low-resistance grounding if needed to operate selective ground relays. In either case the ground-current level should be substantially less than the phase-current fault levels.

The generator may also be applied to a four-wire load without transformation. If the generator is rated for solidly grounded service, the neutral may be connected directly to the grounded circuit conductor. If a standard generator is used, a reactor should be connected between neutral and the grounded circuit conductor so as to limit the momentary ground fault current to no more than the momentary three-phase fault current (see [10] and [8]). When $3i_0 = i"_d$ the value of this neutral reactor, X_N, should be

$$X_N = 1/3 \ (2X''_d - X_2 - X_2) \tag{1}$$

where

$3i_0$	= The ground fault current = $3/(X"_d + X_2 + X_0 + 3X_n)$
$i"_d$	= The three phase subtransient fault current = $1/X"_d$
$X"_d$	= The generator subtransient reactance
X_2	= The generator negative sequence reactance
X_0	= The generator zero sequence reactance

Note that a resistor should not be used for this purpose, since its impedance is in quadrature with the machine reactance and thus would require a much larger value of resistance than reactance. This resistance would incur large losses from the flow of either fault or load current. The zero-sequence load current would also produce an objectionable voltage drop, since the load is primarily resistive.

On the other hand, the neutral reactor will cause little voltage drop to be produced by in-phase zero-sequence load current. The total zero-sequence current will be a small value because the generator has limited unbalanced current capacity. The continuous negative-sequence current capability of generators covered in ANSI C50 standards is 8% or 10%. Salient-pole industrial generators may have slightly higher capacity. The use of the reactor between the generator neutral and the neutral circuit conductor does not affect the NEC [1] requirement that the neutral circuit conductor be solidly grounded.

If generators are solidly grounded, the system's circuit breaker duty must be calculated at the higher ground fault duty.

If the wye side of a delta-wye transformer is connected to a generator that is configured for four-wire service, the generator should be designed with a two-thirds pitch winding. This transformer will act as a short circuit to third-harmonic currents, and without cancellation of third-harmonic voltage, the resultant current may adversely affect ground-fault relaying and generator capacity.

1.8.3 Paralleled Generators in Isolated System

This section covers only those generators that are paralleled to other generators on the same bus. Generators paralleled through transformers would be considered as paralleled to a separate source.

The considerations are similar to 1.8.1 except for the possible circulation of third-harmonic current between solidly grounded generators if any of the generators do not have two-thirds pitch windings. If generators are of identical design, there will be no significant circulation of third-harmonic current while the generators are being operated at identical power and reactive current outputs. If the generators are not of identical design, there will be a third-harmonic circulating current. If identical generators are operated with unequal loading, there will be a third harmonic circulating current. If these currents are not limited by neutral impedance, they may have levels that adversely affect ground relaying or generator thermal capacity. Generators with two-thirds pitch windings have the minimum impedance to the flow of third harmonic currents generated elsewhere due to their low zero-sequence impedance.

High-resistance grounding of the generators will adequately limit these harmonic currents. Thus, it is attractive to use high-resistance grounding on the generators even if there are load feeders directly connected to the generator bus, and to use low-resistance bus grounding to provide selective relaying on the load feeders. Low-resistance grounding of the generators at values not exceeding 25% of generator rating will normally suppress third-harmonic current to adequate values even with dissimilar generators, but the variable ground fault current available with multiple generators may pose a relay-coordination problem.

Where multiple generators are solidly grounded but have switches in the neutral, there has sometimes been the practice of grounding only one of the several generators in parallel to limit ground-fault current duty or circulating third-harmonic current. This will increase the fault-current duty in the grounded generator above that for which it would customarily be rated. A chart showing this difference appears in the *Westinghouse Transmission and Distribution Reference Book* [18]. The ability to switch neutrals appears to invite operational errors that could affect integrity of grounding, allowing overvoltage on four-wire loads, which would result in failure to meet criteria for effective grounding or acceptable reactive grounding and thus would possibly violate the NEC.

1.8.4 Generators as Unparalleled Alternate Sources

This category covers emergency and standby generators that are connected to the loads by transfer switches, which precludes paralleling with the normal source. With three-wire systems the generators would be considered a separately derived source, since there would be no continuous connection through a system neutral. Generator grounding practices would be guided by 1.8.2 and 1.8.3.

Where four-wire systems are involved, it has been shown in IEEE Std 446-1987 [6], Chapter 7, that objectionable currents can flow if a three-pole transfer switch is used. Whether or not the neutral is grounded at the generator as well as at the normal service, ground-fault relaying errors can occur. The NEC does not require neutral grounding at a generator when it has a common neutral with the grounded utility service neutral conductor per Article 250-5(d) and its fine-print note. However, this connection scheme will not allow any repair or testing of the normal system, which involves disconnection from ground of the neutral conductor to the generator if the generator is operating. There is the hazard that workers performing such repair or tests may not be aware that the generator is operating. The use of a four-pole transfer switch can eliminate these problems and is recommended. This will allow generator grounding practices to be in accordance with 1.8.2 and 1.8.3.

1.8.5 Generators Paralleled with Other Sources

This category describes generators connected to transformers that are, or can be, connected to other power sources. While the primary consideration is the generator grounding, decisions can be affected by the necessity of providing the desired grounding on the other side of the transformer while other generating sources may be disconnected.

The use of a delta-wye transformer with the wye facing the generator offers the advantage of providing neutral grounding, solid or impedance, to the generator-fed bus when the generator is not connected. It has the disadvantage of not offering grounding to the system connected to the delta side of the transformer. It presents a hazard if both the transformer and generator neutrals are solidly grounded [23]. The wye winding with a delta primary is a short circuit to any third-harmonic current produced by the generator. The ground-fault duty on the bus will be greater than the arithmetical sum of the ground-fault currents supplied by the transformer and generator when each is connected to the bus independently. The ground-fault current in the generator will exceed that which would occur when the generator is not paralleled. The fault currents must be calculated using symmetrical component techniques as shown in [23] rather than simply using the sum of the admittances of the transformer and generator sources. A generator rated for grounded service not otherwise specified is normally rated for the ground fault current flowing when not paralleled.

A generator neutral reactor can be used to limit the generator-fault duty to an acceptable value as calculated per [23] but may not limit any generated third-harmonic current to an acceptable value. Thus, suppression of third harmonic may be necessary to facilitate adequate ground-fault relaying.

If the delta of the delta wye transformer is connected to the generator bus, neutral grounding is available for the system on the other side of the transformer. However, the generator bus will be ungrounded until such time as the generator is connected. Independent bus grounding will require some form of grounding bank and will produce either effective or impedance grounding. If the grounding bank is connected to the transformer terminals, generator grounding will be dictated by the nature of any load connected to the bus. If the grounding bank is connected to the bus, the generator may be high-resistance grounded.

A wye-wye transformer as shown in Fig 24 can provide grounding to the side opposite the source, whichever side may have the source connected. The disadvantage is that the zero-sequence current must be provided by the source, so that the system grounding required on the other side of the transformer will dictate the type of generator grounding. If a delta tertiary is added to the transformer, this tertiary will supply the zero-sequence current so that the generator can be grounded without regard to system grounding requirements on the other side of the transformer.

The methods of grounding are also described in [3], which covers generator ground-fault protection as well. It should be noted that this standard was developed primarily for utility generators and does not contain some of the considerations for industrial applications.

1.9 System Grounding for Uninterruptible Power Systems[2]

1.9.1 General

As with any electrical system, correct grounding procedures are essential to the overall safety and operation of an Uninterruptible Power System (UPS). In particular, personnel safety, equipment protection, and sensitive electronic system performance can all be jeopardized by incorrect or ineffective grounding systems. The grounding of the UPS is very important when such systems supply power to critical computer loads.

To illustrate the recommended practices, several schemes are presented, based on various source and load configurations, for properly grounding the on-line UPS. These schemes do not cover every possible configuration but only present some basic guidelines; UPS systems, particularly new designs, may have configurations that require different grounding schemes. The NEC and applicable local codes must be followed as interpreted by the local enforcement authorities.

In the grounding schemes presented, the grounded conductor is part of the current-carrying circuit. The term *grounded conductor* refers to that leg of the circuit (usually the neutral) that is intentionally connected to ground. The grounding conductor is not part of the current-carrying circuit. The term *grounding conductor* refers to the conductor(s) that connect(s) all exposed metal parts of a device to ground; primarily for safety, secondarily for performance.

1.9.2 Significant NEC requirements

1) Separately Derived Source—Article 250–5(d) of the NEC defines a separately-derived source:
   A premises wiring system whose power is derived from generator, transformer, or converter windings and has no direct electrical connection, including a solidly-connected grounded circuit conductor, to supply conductors originating in another (grounded) system …
2) NEC Ground Requirement — It is a requirement of the NEC [1] that the grounded circuit conductor (normally the neutral) of a separately derived source be bonded at its source to the equipment safety grounding conductor and to a local grounding electrode conductor that is connected to the nearest effectively grounded: (1) building steel, (2) metal water pipe, and (3) other man-made grounding electrode (connection to earth).

---

[2]The material in this section is adapted from *Technical/Application News* [23]. It is used with the permission of the Liebert Corporation.

3) Specific NEC Provision—The NEC prohibits connecting the grounded circuit conductor (neutral) to the grounding conductor at more than one point. If the neutral were connected to the grounding conductor at more than one point, some of the normal neutral current would be allowed to flow in the grounding conductor circuit between the points of connection. Besides being a safety hazard, this practice defeats ground-fault protection schemes [29].

4) UPS Classification—The most common UPS module has a wye-connected inverter output and often requires the bypass input to be fed from a wye-connected source. The inverter portion of the UPS module is a separately derived source, in that the input to the rectifier/charger is electrically isolated from the inverter output. However, because the bypass input neutral is directly connected to the inverter output neutral, the UPS as a system may or may not be considered a separately derived system, depending on the particular arrangement for the bypass input neutral. Since this configuration of UPS encounters the most severe grounding problems, it will be used in the sample grounding schemes.

1.9.3 Grounding Schemes

1.9.3.1 Configuration 1

Single UPS Module, Nonisolated Bypass, Grounded Wye-Service. In this arrangement (Fig 9), a grounded-wye service is connected to both the main input and bypass (reserve) input of a single UPS module, and the Power Distribution Center does not contain an isolation transformer. The neutral, which is bonded to the grounding conductor at the service entrance equipment, is brought into the UPS module.

1.9.3.1.1 *Grounded/Grounding Conductor Arrangement.*

Since the UPS module output neutral is solidly connected to the bypass input (service entrance) neutral, the UPS module is not considered a separately derived system according to the NEC. In this system, (1) the UPS neutral should not be bonded to the equipment grounding conductor, and (2) no local grounding electrode conductor should be installed to the UPS module.

1.9.3.1.2 *Features/Performance.*

While this arrangement may be typical for 208 V input/208 V output UPS systems, it does not provide any isolation or common mode noise attenuation for sensitive loads. It appears that ground-fault current from the inverter may adversely affect the service entrance ground fault relay as shown in IEEE Std 446-1987 [6], Chapter 7, for emergency generators. Actually, the inverter will not supply ground-fault current since the static switch will transfer because of the fault-depressed voltage.

1.9.3.2 Configuration 2

Single UPS Module, Isolated Bypass. In this configuration (Fig 10), a bypass transformer is used to feed the bypass input of the UPS module. The bypass transformer and UPS module together constitute a separately derived system, since there is no direct electrical connection between the input (service entrance) circuit conductors and the output circuit conductors.

1.9.3.2.1 *Grounded/Grounding Conductor Arrangement.*

Since this configuration is considered a separately derived source, the neutral of the UPS module should be bonded to the equipment grounding conductor, and a local grounding electrode module should be installed, per NEC [1], 250-26. (In this particular system, the bonding of the neutral to the grounding conductor could be done at either the bypass transformer or at the UPS module. The UPS module is chosen for the point of bonding because it is in the normal power flow and is electrically closer to the load.) The bypass transformer is used in the bypass input to provide isolation and to step down the voltage if required (for example, in a 480 V input/208 V output configuration).

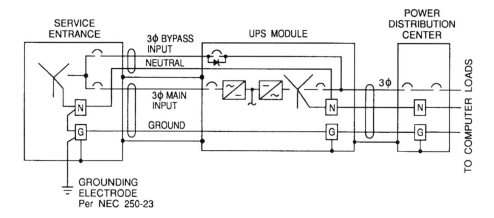

Figure 9—Configuration 1

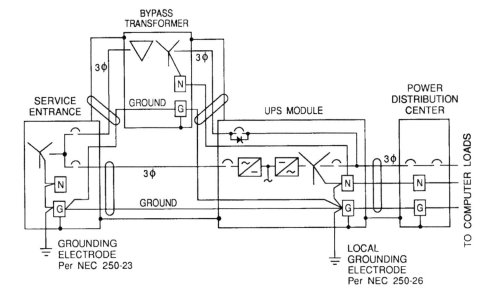

Figure 10—Configuration 2

1.9.3.2.2 *Features/Performance.*

With this arrangement, isolation from the input is achieved, and common-mode noise attenuation can be obtained for the sensitive loads if the UPS and bypass transformer are located electrically close (recommendation is 50 ft (15.2 m) or less) to the Power Distribution Center and the sensitive loads.

1.9.3.3 Configuration 3

Single UPS Module, Nonisolated Bypass, Isolated Distribution Center. In Configuration 3 (Fig 11, the UPS module main input and bypass input are connected to a grounded wye service in the same manner as Configuration 1.

1.9.3.3.1 *Ground/Grounding Conductor Arrangement.*

As explained in Configuration 1, the UPS module is not considered to be a separately derived source, since the neutral is bonded to the grounding conductor at the service entrance equipment and is solidly connected to the UPS module output neutral. Therefore, the UPS neutral would not be bonded to the equipment grounding conductor in the UPS module. However, the Power Distribution Center is provided with an isolation transformer and is considered a separately derived source. Therefore, the Power Distribution Center neutral should be bonded to the equipment grounding conductor and should be connected to a local grounding electrode in compliance with the NEC [1], 250–26.

1.9.3.3.2 *Features/Performance.*

This arrangement can be applied to 208 V input/208 V output UPS modules, as well as to 480 V input/480 V output UPS modules. (The voltage stepdown to 208 V occurs in the Power Distribution Center.) The common-mode noise attenuation of this arrangement is better than Configuration I or Configuration 2, since the isolation (common-mode rejection) occurs as close to the load as is practical. Using this configuration, the UPS module can be located remotely from the Power Distribution Center without compromising the common-mode noise performance. Also, by using 480 V input/480 V output UPS modules, smaller and less costly power feeders can be used and less voltage drop (as a percent of nominal) can be obtained. This is the preferred arrangement when using UPS modules and Power Distribution Centers.

1.9.3.4 Configuration 4

Single UPS Module, 3-Wire Bypass, Isolated Distribution Center, Grounded-Wye Service. Configuration 4 is similar to Configuration 3 except that the service entrance neutral is not included in the bypass input power feed.

1.9.3.4.1 *Grounded/Grounding Conductor Arrangement.*

In this configuration, the neutral of the service entrance equipment is not brought into the UPS module. The UPS module is, therefore, considered a separately derived source. As such, the neutral should be bonded to the equipment grounding conductor, and a local grounding electrode conductor should be installed in accordance with the NEC [1], 250-26. Since the Power Distribution Center contains an isolation transformer, it also is a separately derived source. This neutral should also be bonded to the equipment grounding conductor and to a local grounding electrode.

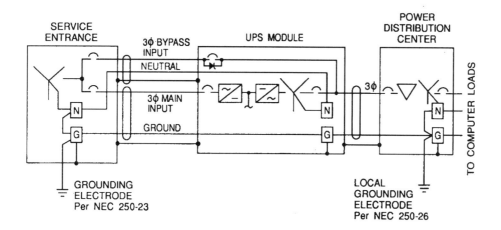

Figure 11—Configuration 3

1.9.3.4.2 *Features/Performance.*

The scheme shown in Fig 12 serves as an alternative to the scheme shown in Fig 11 when no neutral is available for the bypass input, provided that (1) the main input and bypass input are fed from the same source, (2) the source is a solidly grounded wye source, and (3) no neutral is required for the UPS load.

With some UPS systems, the neutral should be included with the bypass input, even if not required for the output, because the neutral is used for sensing and monitoring of the bypass input.

As in Configuration 3, since the Power Distribution Center contains an isolation transformer, isolation and common-mode noise reduction occurs when the center is located as close to the load as is practical.

1.9.3.5 Configuration 5

Single UPS Module, Isolated Bypass, Delta-Connected Source (Fig 13). Configuration 5 is similar to Configuration 2, with the exception that the input power source (service entrance) is delta connected. Most UPS modules require that the bypass input be fed from a wye-connected source. Therefore, when the UPS module is used with other than a wye-connected source, the bypass input must be fed from a bypass transformer with a wye-connected secondary.

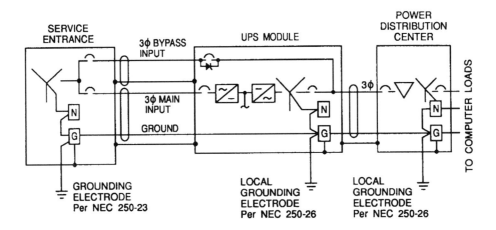

Figure 12—Configuration 4

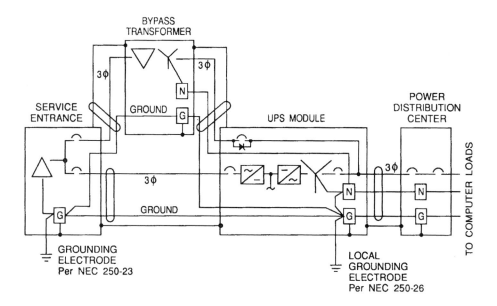

Figure 13—Configuration 5

1.9.3.5.1 *Grounded/Grounding Conductor Arrangement.*

In this configuration, as in Configuration 2, the UPS module neutral should be bonded to the equipment grounding conductor, and a local grounding electrode conductor should be installed in accordance with the NEC [1], 250–26.

1.9.3.5.2 *Features/Performance.*

With this arrangement, as in Configuration 2, isolation from the input is achieved, and common-mode noise attenuation can be obtained for the sensitive loads if the UPS and bypass transformer are located electrically close (recommended 50 ft (15.2 m) or less) to the Power Distribution Center and to the sensitive loads.

1.9.3.6 Configuration 6

Multiple-Module UPS System Example. In general, a multiple-module UPS system may be thought of as being an extension of a particular single-module system, except that the UPS "block" is now composed of more than one UPS module, and everything (including the bypass) feeds through a stand-alone static transfer switch. As an example consider Fig 14 as the multiple-module extension of the same grounding scheme shown in Fig 12.

1.9.3.6.1 *Grounded/Grounding Conductor Arrangement.*

Fig 14 illustrates one of the grounding schemes for multiple UPS modules with a stand-alone static switch. In this configuration, the bypass transformer and UPS modules I and 2 are considered to be a separately derived system, since there is no direct electrical connection between the input and output circuit conductors In order to provide a central point for bonding the UPS output neutral to the ground for the entire UPS scheme, the stand-alone static switch is utilized. (When the neutral is bonded to the grounding conductor in the stand-alone static switch, full-size neutrals must be run from the UPS modules and bypass transformer to the static switch, regardless of whether the neutral is required for the static switch loads.) The neutral-to-grounding-conductor bond and the local grounding electrode conductor should be installed in accordance with the NEC [1], 250–26.

1.9.3.6.2 *Features/Performance.*

Using the static switch to provide the central point for bonding the neutral to the grounding conductor as in this sample multiple-UPS module configuration, a UPS module could be removed from, or added to, the overall scheme without jeopardizing the integrity of the grounding system.

Depending upon the multiple-module configuration, the grounding concepts of single-model configurations 1 through 5 can be applied.

1.9.3.7 Configuration 7

Multiple-Module 415 Hz UPS System. In Configuration 7 (Fig 15), the 415 Hz UPS module main input is connected to the grounded wye service in the same manner as the previous 60 Hz UPS configurations. No bypass feed is used with 415 Hz UPS modules.

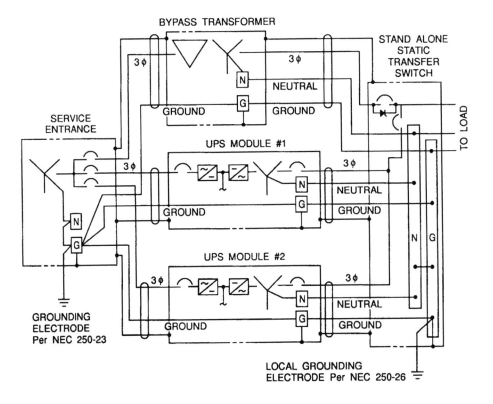

Figure 14—Configuration 6

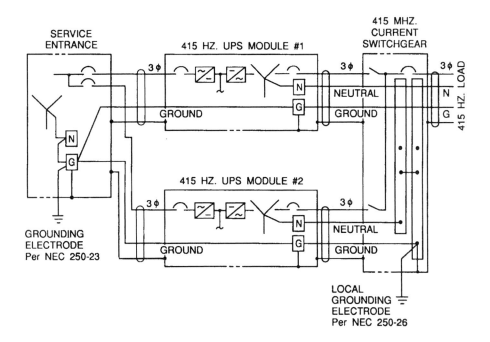

Figure 15—Configuration 7

1.9.3.7.1 *Grounded/Grounding Conductor Arrangement.*

In this configuration, there is no bypass feeder, so the neutral of the service entrance equipment is not connected to the UPS output neutral. The UPS module is, therefore, considered a separately derived source. As such, the UPS output neutral should be bonded to the equipment grounding conductor, and a local grounding electrode conductor should be installed in accordance with the NEC [1], 250-26. In this case, both UPS modules would meet the NEC requirements for a separately derived source. To provide a central point for bonding the UPS output neutral to the ground for the entire UPS system, the neutral-to-grounding-conductor bond should be made in the output switchgear. (If a single 415 Hz UPS module is used, the neutral-to-grounding-conductor bond should be made inside the UPS module.)

1.9.3.7.2 *Features/Performance.*

Using the output switchgear to provide the central point for bonding the neutral to the grounding conductor allows a UPS module to be removed or added to the parallel system without jeopardizing the integrity of the grounding scheme.

1.9.3.8 Configuration 8

Single UPS Module wit Maintenance Bypass Switchgear. In Configuration 8 (Fig 16), maintenance bypass switchgear is used to completely isolate the UPS module from the critical ac load during maintenance and off-line testing. A grounded-wye service is connected to the main input and bypass input of a single UPS module and to the maintenance bypass switchgear. If the neutral is required for the critical load, the neutral (which is bonded to the grounding conductor at the service entrance equipment) is brought into the UPS module and the maintenance bypass switchgear.

31

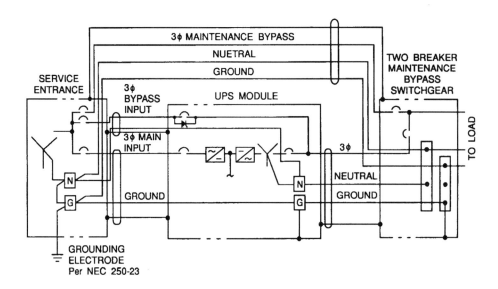

Figure 16—Configuration 8 (Four Wire)

1.9.3.8.1 *Grounded/Grounding Conductor Arrangement.*

Since the UPS output neutral and the maintenance bypass switchgear neutral are connected to the service entrance neutral, the UPS module is not considered a separately derived system according to the NEC. In this system (1) the neutrals of the UPS output and the maintenance bypass switchgear should not be bonded to the equipment grounding conductor, and (2) no local grounding electrode conductor should be installed.

1.9.3.8.2 *Features/Performance.*

This arrangement does not provide any isolation or common-mode noise attenuation for sensitive loads. If a Power Distribution Center with an isolation transformer is provided downstream from the UPS system (near the sensitive load), the common-mode noise attenuation of this arrangement would be greatly improved. Also, since the Power Distribution Center with transformer requires only a three-phase, three-wire plus ground input, the neutral conductor would not need to be connected from the service entrance to the UPS bypass and from the service entrance or the UPS output to the maintenance bypass switchgear (see Fig 17).

1.10 Multi-Voltage Systems

In any system the voltage may not be uniform throughout the system due to voltage drops caused by current flowing through system impedances. These voltage differences will normally be insignificant compared to the voltage imposed across the insulation between conductor and ground. However, the voltage can be changed significantly without creating a separate system, usually by use of an autotransformer or by connecting in series two significant reactances of opposite sign.

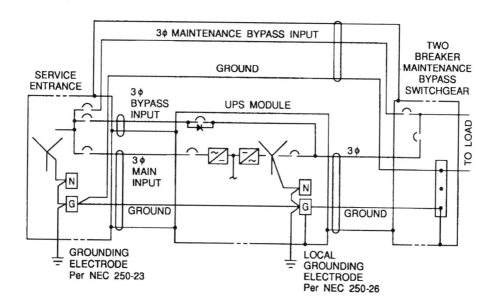

Figure 17—Configuration 8 (Three Wire)

1.10.1 Autotransformers

Occasionally autotransformers will be used to transform voltage, usually to reduce transformer cost, or perhaps to avoid creating a new grounding system. Unless the system grounding is suitable for the use of an autotransformer and the autotransformer is properly applied, its use may seriously reduce grounding and ground relaying effectiveness and expose equipment to a voltage-to-ground level higher than that for which it is designed.

The three-phase wye autotransformer with no delta tertiary has extremely high zero sequence impedance if no connection is made to its neutral. Fig 18 shows that a ground fault at A' will cause the source line-to-ground voltage to be imposed across the A–A' section of the autotransformer. Should that section of the winding be able to support this voltage, then the voltage to ground at N, the neutral of the autotransformer, would rise in proportion to the turns ratio of A'–N to A–A', and B' and C' would have voltages to ground higher than B and C, the high voltage level. The secondary line-to-line voltage can also be increased.

In normal practice, winding A–A' would not support the full voltage, but would instead saturate, thus passing a certain amount of zero sequence current. In the process, it will create high-frequency components of voltage, at which frequency the winding can support a voltage proportional to that frequency. Thus, a very high voltage to ground could still exist at N.

Even if the secondary of the autotransformer is the higher voltage, it will still be overvoltaged by a secondary line-to-ground fault as shown in Chapter 6 of Beeman [10]. This reference also points out that overvoltages can also be caused by transient surges, such as from switching or lightning, being impressed across the section of winding between primary and secondary connections.

Figure 19 shows that when a source to a step-down autotransformer is impedance grounded, a ground on the source side of the autotransformer can cause the voltage from B' and C' to ground to approach the line-to-line voltage of the source. If the autotransformer steps up the voltage, the voltage to ground on the lower voltage system will lie between that shown in Fig 20 and what might be achieved in Fig 18 depending upon the relation of the grounding impedance to the exciting impedance of the autotransformer.

Figures 21 and 22 show that delta autotransformers do not offer a reduction in voltage to ground on the lower voltage system commensurate with the reduction in phase voltage, thus reducing the cost benefit of choosing the autotransformer rather than a full transformer. The open-delta version offers no reduction in maximum voltage to ground, but does result in an unbalanced voltage to ground that might be undesirable. In neither case do ground faults cause increased voltages to appear across the transformer windings, and line-to-ground voltage at either voltage will not exceed the higher line-to-line voltage. Should a full transformer be used in either case, it might be possible to reduce the class of insulation in the lower voltage system. In all the above examples there is a safety hazard due to normal perceptions of the relation of maximum voltage to the normal voltage on a circuit. For this reason, the NEC [1] has imposed restrictions as to how autotransformers can be used.

Figure 23 shows the correct configuration for using an autotransformer. There must be an effective connection between the neutral of the autotransformer and the neutral of the source transformer for flow of zero-sequence current. In an industrial installation where the NEC would apply, the connection must be made by extending the neutral of the source transformer. No ground connection must be made at the autotransformer to comply with Section 250-23 of the NEC [1]. A circuit supplied by an autotransformer would not appear to meet the criteria of a separately derived system.

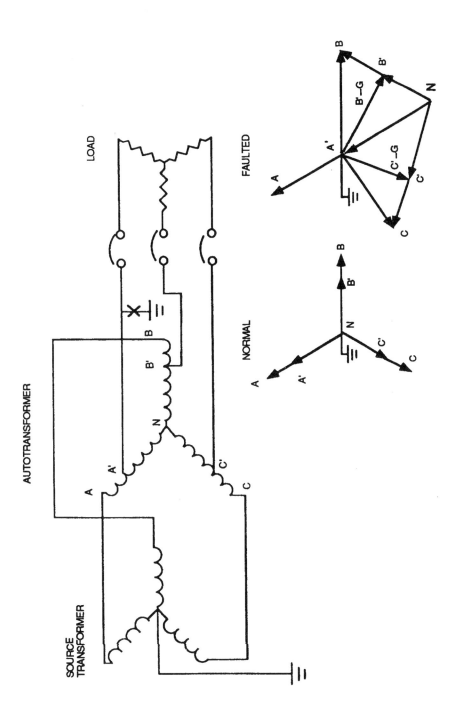

Figure 18—Ungrounded Wye Step-Down Autotransformer Normal Phasor Relations

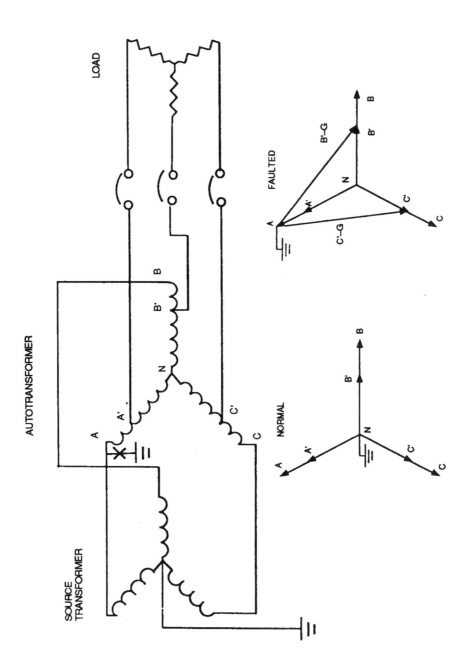

**Figure 19—Ungrounded Wye Step-Down Autotransformer
Phasors with Primary Ground Fault**

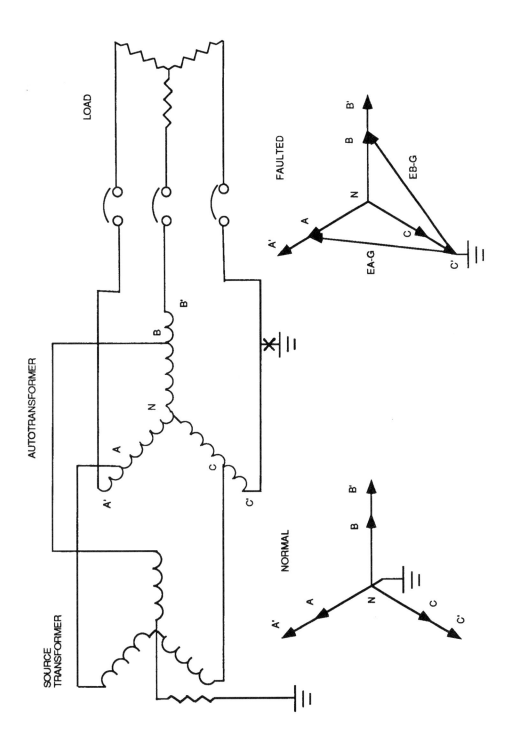

**Figure 20—Ungrounded Wye Step-Up Autotransformer
Normal and Fault Phasors**

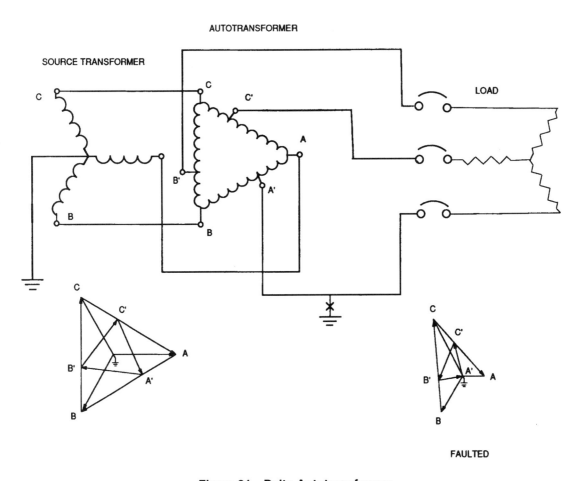

Figure 21—Delta Autotransformer

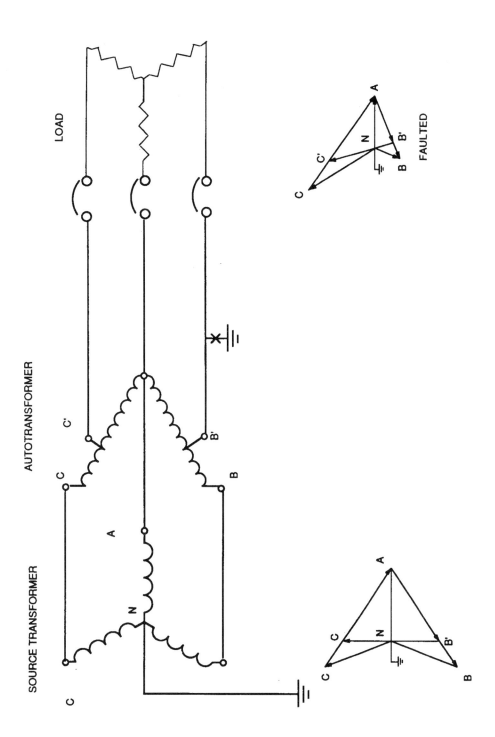

Figure 22—Open Delta Autotransformer

1.10.2 Wye-Wye Transformers

The wye-wye transformer is shown in Fig 24 with the primary and secondary neutrals interconnected and grounded. This transformer configuration is used on solidly grounded utility distribution systems, particularly underground systems, to prevent ferroresonance when the supply switches can be operated one pole at a time. The utilities ground the primary neutral point to minimize the neutral-to-earth voltage throughout the length of the distribution line and by default on underground systems using bare concentric neutral cables. They ground the secondary neutral to provide an effectively grounded low-voltage service. Note. that this multiple grounding of the primary at each transformer is not essential to prevent ferroresonance or provide secondary grounding as long as the fourth conductor is brought to the primary neutral of the transformer. The neutral-to-transformer case and ground connection minimizes secondary neutral-to-ground voltage during a fault between primary and transformer case.

In an industrial distribution system, the physical length of the circuit will usually be short enough so that excessive neutral-to-ground voltages will not be present even if the transformer common neutral is not grounded. Section 250-23 of the NEC [1] normally prohibits grounding of the neutral on the load side of the service disconnect, but Section 250-152(2) allows multigrounding of the neutral of an outdoor overhead line or direct burial cable with bare neutral if the circuit voltage is over 1000 V.

With a continuous connection from the source neutral to the primary and secondary neutrals of the wye-wye transformer, the output of the transformer would not constitute a separately derived system as defined in Section 250-5(d) of the NEC [1]. If the neutral is grounded at the source, the output of the wye-wye transformer will be a continuation of the grounded system, though at the secondary voltage of the transformer. It is quite similar in performance to the autotransformer shown in Fig 25 except that it provides the added safety of having the only metallic connection between primary and secondary at the neutral point.

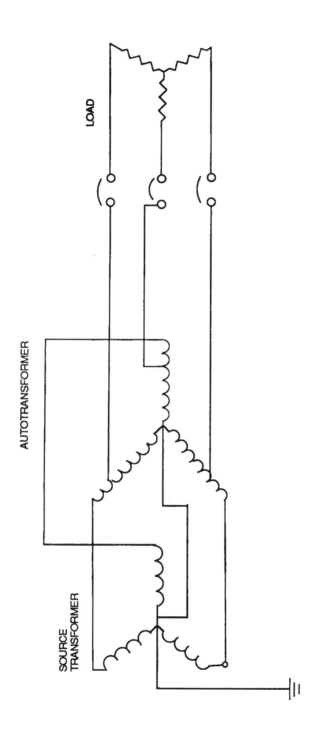

**Figure 23—Wye Autotransformer
Grounded Neutral Four-Wire Connection**

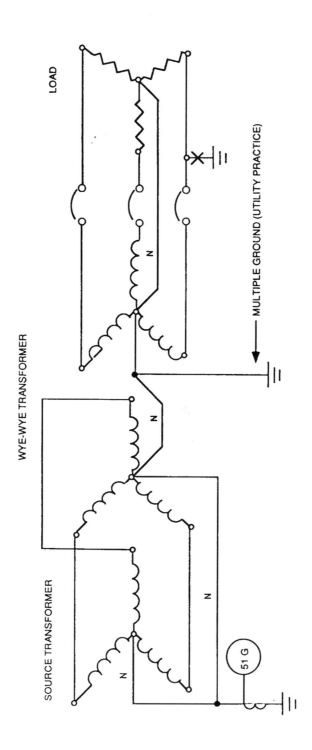

**Figure 24—Grounded Wye-Grounded Wye Transformer
Multigrounded Common Neutral**

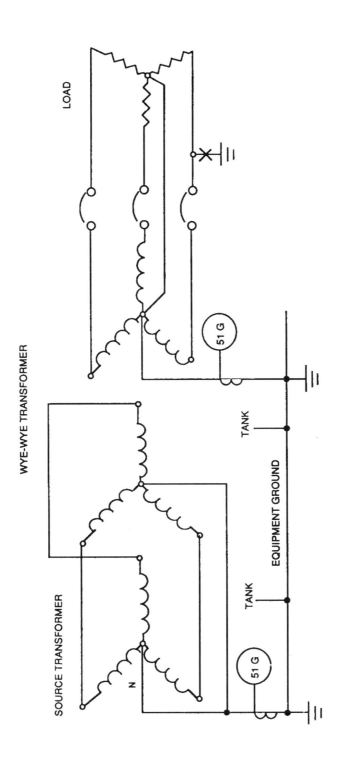

**Figure 25—Grounded Wye-Grounded Wye Transformers
Separately Grounded Neutrals**

The circuit supplied by the wye-wye transformer shown in Fig 25 should be considered a separately derived system, since there is no direct metallic connection between primary and secondary of the transformer. Primary and secondary ground faults are separately measured and relayed. The output of the secondary will not be grounded unless a connection to earth is made from the secondary of the transformer. The secondary could be impedance grounded. Secondary neutral grounding will also require a connection from the neutral of the primary source to the primary neutral of the wye-wye transformer to supply zero-sequence current. Unlike the delta-wye transformer, the wye-wye transformer itself is not a source of zero-sequence current. Grounding can be achieved without a primary neutral connection if a phase of the secondary rather than the neutral is grounded, since no zero-sequence current is involved. The effect is then identical to corner grounding of a delta-delta transformer.

If a delta tertiary is added to a wye-wye transformer it will not be necessary to supply zero-sequence current from the primary source, since the tertiary will act as a source of zero sequence current.

Thus, the wye-wye transformer can be considered a part of a single multi-voltage system if the neutrals are interconnected or can be considered to create a separate system if they are not. The symmetry of the wye-wye allows it to provide grounding for its load-side system even though the source and load side may be interchanged at any time.

1.10.3 "Resonantly" Produced Voltages

This term is applied to the voltage that will appear at the junction between reactances of opposite sign connected in series even though the reactances may not actually be resonant at the supply frequency. The variance of the voltage with respect to the supply voltage will be a function of how close the elements are to resonance and the ratio (Q) of inductive reactance to the resistance.

A common instance is the use of series capacitors on low power factor loads where random switching or other variations create objectionable voltage excursions. Fig 26 represents the circuit of a spot welder whose inductance is fixed by the dimensions of the machine but whose resistive load can be varied. With full power-factor correction, the voltage rise across the capacitor will be 1.732E at 0.5 power factor and 4.9E at 0.2 power factor. With the ground fault as shown, this 4.9E across the capacitor will be impressed between the source transformer and ground. Both the transformer and its grounding impedance will be subjected to overvoltage. For this reason, such series capacitors should be used only on effectively grounded systems, which will limit the voltage rise to safe values.

A more commonly observed series reactance circuit is created when a capacitive load is connected, usually for power factor and/or voltage correction. Since these capacitors are in series with the source reactance of the power system, the voltage is caused to rise. The voltage rise caused by the normal size of power factor capacitors would not be expected to exceed 5%–10% under the worst conditions, since the system is not approaching resonance at the fundamental power frequency. This is not a different voltage class and does not present a hazard. Its discussion here is only to present a familiar example of reactances in series.

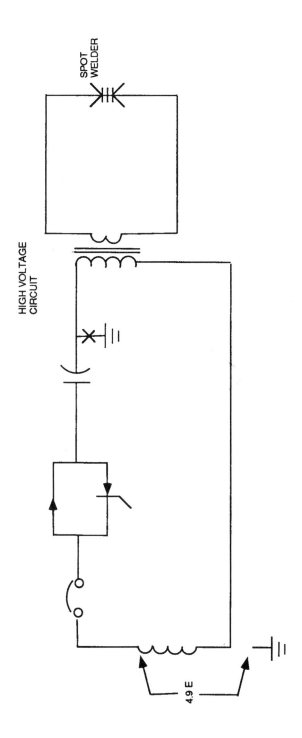

Figure 26—Series Capacitor Resistance Welder

Resonance can be achieved by the addition of power factor capacitors at multiples of the power system frequency. When there are sources of harmonics, such as nonlinear loads, the resulting harmonic voltages can be raised by a resonant condition. Such voltages would not normally reach hazardous values. A hazardous level, should it occur, would be rapidly reduced by overcurrents in the capacitors causing failures or fuse operations, thus detuning the circuit.

Impulse voltages can be amplified and extended as damped oscillations (ringing) by resonant circuits. These voltages can exceed insulation capabilities.

Resonant conditions prone to continuous oscillation due to lack of resistive loading (damping) can be triggered by switching or by system failures. The most common example is that created by single-phase switching of transformer primaries when there is no secondary load. This produces the "ferroresonant" condition where the excitation impedance of the transformer interacts with the capacitance of the primary cable.

These resonantly produced voltages are not considered as system, or useful, voltages, with the exception of the resistance welder application. Thus, they do not create multi-voltage systems, but are discussed here so that they might be avoided. With the exception of increasing the impulse capability of the insulation, the main defense against these voltages is suppression.

There are other situations where high voltages can be produced by inadvertently created resonant conditions. These are usually the result of insulation, equipment failures, or unintended circuit configurations. The voltages are more extreme if conditions at or close to resonance are achieved. When the inductive element has an iron core, the inductance can vary when the iron is saturated due to the high voltage, which at the same time causes nonsinusoidal current with resulting harmonics. This can result in arriving at a resonant condition referred to as "ferroresonance." These are not "system voltages" as have been discussed in the preceding paragraphs, since they are unintended and may be transitory in nature.

In some cases, occurrence of these voltages can be affected or eliminated by the grounding design, but such changes in voltage also may involve choice of transformer design or performance of switching devices. A common cause of ferroresonance is the impressing of voltage across a transformer winding and a conductor capacitance to ground, the conductor having been disconnected from its normal source. If the transformer is wye connected, grounding of the neutral will usually prevent voltage being impressed across this series connection. A resonant condition produced by a grounded coil acting in series with the line-to-ground capacitance of an ungrounded system can be alleviated if the capacitance is shunted by grounding the system.

1.11 Portable Mining Equipment Supply Systems

The concept of protecting mine electrical equipment and personnel by suitable grounding has existed since electricity was first introduced into mines. As early as 1916, the U.S. Bureau of Mines recommended equipment frame grounding as a means of preventing electrical shock to miners working on or around electrical equipment [13]. Adequate grounding has been a difficult problem for the mining industry, sometimes more complex and challenging than for other industries. Hazards associated with ground faults are amplified by the portable and mobile nature of these power systems, and system and equipment grounding are interrelated. A surface-mine machine can have a substantial power demand (e.g., 18 000 hp) at potentials up to 25 kV or greater. The power demand of an underground mining machine can exceed 1100 hp at potentials up to 4160 V. The portable equipment must be designed to permit personnel to approach (and touch) apparatus structures without risk of electric shock. This section will emphasize the grounding aspects of the supply system, whereas 2.6 will cover related equipment-grounding information. Reference [22] provides extensive details about both subjects.

A simplified arrangement of a mine power system is shown in Fig 27. Sub-stations are employed to transform the incoming utility voltage to a distribution level. Mine distribution is almost always expanded radial, and overhead lines (surface mines) or cables (surface and underground mines) are used to supply switchhouses (portable switchgear) located near load concentrations. In typical underground mines, switchhouses are connected via portable cables to portable power centers, which supply lower voltage through trailing cables to the utilization equipment (e.g., continuous miners, longwalls, load-haul-dump units, etc.). In surface mines, large utilization equipment, such as shovels and draglines, are often powered at the distribution voltage, and a trailing cable completes the power circuit from the switchhouse to the machine. (As with underground mines, portable substations or power centers are used when distribution and utilization levels are different.)

The recommended grounding technique for these portable or mobile equipment applications is a safety ground system that employs resistance grounding. Fig 27 illustrates the concept (overload and short-circuit protection are not shown for clarity of the grounding systems and associated protective relaying). The substation contains two separate ground beds, maintained some distance apart. Substation surge arrestors, fencing, and equipment frames are tied to the system ground bed, typically located under the substation area. The substation transformer is either delta-wye, delta-delta, or wye-delta connected (wye-wye is not recommended), and the secondary neutral (direct or derived) is tied to the safety ground bed through the neutral grounding resistor. Each ac equipment frame in the distribution system is connected via grounding conductors to the safety ground bed. The station bed is intended to handle lightning, other transformer-primary surge conditions, and primary-system line-to-ground faults. The purpose of the safety bed is maintaining equipment frames at near earth potential, and a low bed resistance is important so dangerous potentials are not developed on machine frames. Separation between the system and safety ground beds is needed to isolate high system-ground voltage rise (a temporary rise of 5 kV or more is not unusual) from the bed. This resistance is recommended as 5.0 Ω or less (see [20] and [19]). It is not unusual to find that a much greater distance is required to provide needed separation [16]. The design of these ground beds is complex, and many variables must be examined to derive an optimum configuration (see [15] and [14]). The references cited in this paragraph should be consulted. IEEE Std 367-1987 (ANSI) [4] also contains important information about ground-bed separation in regard to the influence of a ground potential rise of a ground electrode.

At each transformation step within the distribution system, such as in a portable power center, an additional neutral point is established at the transformer secondary. The neutral is tied through a grounding resistor to the equipment frame and, thus, via the grounding conductors to the safety ground bed.

Because of the extensive use of cable distribution and the attendant capacitance from line to ground, ground-fault current limits are higher than that which was recommended for high-resistance grounding earlier in this chapter. United States practice specifies a different maximum current limit depending on the system voltage. When the system voltage is greater than 1000 V, ground current is limited so frame potentials within that system portion do not exceed 100 V during ground-fault conditions. For practical purposes (assuming a 2 Ω grounding-conductor impedance), this restricts the maximum ground-current limit to not more than 50 A; however, most substations serving mines use a 25 A ground-current limit. For power-system segments at or below 1000 V, the ground-current limit must be 25 A or less, but typical practice is 15 A (also see 2.6). Distribution and utilization (mining) equipment in surface mines is typically greater than 1000 V. Underground-mine distribution is almost always greater than 1000 V, whereas mining equipment is usually 1000 V or less.

Correct selection and coordination of protective circuitry are essential to the safety ground system. Regardless of where a ground fault occurs, ground-fault current is primarily limited by the grounding resistor, and selective coordination at each voltage level by the pickup setting alone is normally impossible. The common ground-fault relaying pickup is 40% of the ground-current limit, and time settings are relied on for multistage protection. Regulations should be consulted before selecting specific ground-fault protection schemes. (See [22] and [11].) A typical relaying arrangement is included in Fig 27 [22].

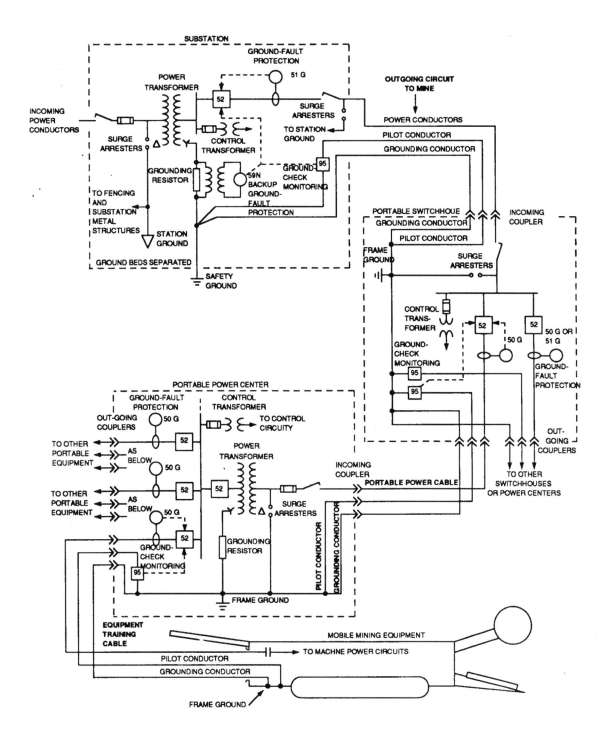

**Figure 27—A Simplified Mine Power Distribution System with a Safety Grounded System
(Overcurrent and Short-Circuit Protection Schemes Are Omitted for Simplicity)**

Zero-sequence relaying (usually instantaneous) establishes primary ground-fault protection for the utilization circuit. Although not shown, back-up protection may also be employed (or required) here by adding a time-delayed zero-sequence relaying at the secondary of the power-center transformer or potential relaying about the grounding resistor. For the distribution system, primary ground-fault protection in the switchhouse establishes a zone of protection for each outgoing circuit; again zero-sequence relaying (instantaneous or minimum time-dial setting) is typically used. Time-delayed zero-sequence or residual relaying in the substation gives both back-up protection for downstream relaying within the distribution safety ground. United States federal regulations specify separation by distance; for example, a minimum of 25 ft (7.6 m) and a "low resistance" for each system and primary ground-fault protection for the zone between its location and the switchhouse. The potential relaying shown about the grounding resistor also provides back-up protection (both relays are sometimes required in the substation). In order for the safety ground system to be effective, grounding conductors must be continuous, and ground-check monitors (relays) are used to verify continuity. Pilot conductors are shown with each monitor, but these are not needed in instances where pilotless relays are applied. All these sensors act to trip the associated circuit interrupter and remove all power to the affected system segment.

The correct operation of the safety ground system relies on three concepts.

1) The earth cannot be used as a grounding conductor.
2) The grounding system serving portable and mobile equipment must be kept isolated.
3) Ground-fault protection must be provided on each outgoing circuit from the substation.

These criteria are sometimes difficult to achieve when other loads are being supplied from a mine substation transformer, such as preparation plants and ventilation fans. Regardless, each is particularly important when an underground mine is connected to the substation. To ensure grounding-system integrity, it is best that underground mine distribution be fed from a separate transformer secondary winding.

1.12 References

[1] ANSI/NFPA 70-1990, The National Electrical Code.[3]

[2] IEEE Std 100-1988, IEEE Standard Dictionary of Electrical and Electronic Terms—4th ed. (ANSI).[4]

[3] IEEE C37.101-1985 (Reaff. 1991), Guide for Generator Ground Protection (ANSI).

[4] IEEE Std 367-1987, IEEE Recommended Practice for Determining the Electric Power Station Ground Potential Rise and Induced Voltage from a Power Fault (ANSI).

[5] IEEE Std 399-1990, IEEE Recommended Practice for Industrial and Commercial Power System Analysis, (IEEE Brown Book) (ANSI).

[6] IEEE Std 446-1987, IEEE Recommended Practice for Emergency and Standby Power Systems (IEEE Orange Book) (ANSI).

[7] P1100/Draft 5, Recommended Practice for Powering and Grounding Sensitive Electronic Equipment, Feb. 1992.[5]

[8] NEMA MG 1-1987, Motors and Generators, Part 22.[6]

---

[3]NFPA publications are available from Publications Sales, National Fire Protection Association, 1 Batterymarch Park, P.O. Box 9101, Quincy, M.A 02269-9101, USA.
[4]IEEE publications are available from the IEEE Service Center, 445 Hoes Lane, P.O. Box 1331, Piscataway, NJ 08855-1331.
[5]This authorized standards project was not approved by the IEEE Standards Board at the time this went to press. It is available from the IEEE Service Center.
[6]NEMA publications are available from the National Electrical Manufacturers Association, 2101 L Street NW, Washington, DC 20037, USA.

[9] AIEE Committee Report, "Application of Ground Fault Neutralizers," *Electrical Engineering*, vol. 72, July 1953, p. 606.

[10] Beeman, D., Editor. *Industrial Power Systems Handbook*. New York: McGraw-Hill, 1955.

[11] Carson, D. B., and Vidergar, J. A. "Considerations of Ground Fault Protection as Influenced by the Occupational Safety and Health Act and the Mining Enforcement and Safety Administration," *IEEE Transactions on Industry Applications*, vol. IA-11, no. 67, Nov./Dec. 1975, p. 108.

[12] Christie, C. V. *Electrical Engineering. 5th ed*. New York: McGraw-Hill, 1938.

[13] Clark, H. H. and Means, C. M. "Suggested Safety Rules for Installing and Using Electrical Equipment in Bituminous Coal Mines," T. P. 138, U.S. Bureau of Mines, Wash., D.C., 1916.

[14] Cooley, W. H. and Hill, H. W., Jr. "Coupling of Mine Grounds to Surface Grounds," *IEEE Transactions on Industry Applications*, vol. IA-22, Mar./Apr. 1986, p. 360.

[15] Cooley, W. L. "Design Considerations Regarding Separation of Mine Safety Ground and Substation Ground Systems," *IEEE IAS Conference Record*, Annual Meeting, Oct. 1977.

[16] Cooley, W. L. and King, R. L. Guide to Substation Grounding and Bonding in Mine Power Systems, IC8835, 1980.

[17] Dick, W. K. and Winter, D. F. "Computation, Measurement and Mitigation of Neutral-to-Earth Potentials on Electrical Distribution Systems," *IEEE Transactions on Power Delivery*, vol. PWRD-2, No. 2, Apr. 1987.

[18] *Electrical Transmission and Distribution Reference Book*, 4th Ed., Westinghouse Elect. Corp., Chapters 2 and 6.

[19] King, R. L., Hill, H. W., Bafana, R. R. and Cooley, W. L. *Guide for Construction of Driven-Rod Ground Beds*, IC8767. Wash., D.C.: U.S. Bureau of Mines, 1978.

[20] Lordi, A. C. "How to Safely Ground Mine Power Systems," *Coal Age*, vol. 68, no. 9, Sep. 1963, p. 110–117.

[21] McFadden, R. H. "Grouping of Generators Connected to Industrial Plant Distribution Buses," *IEEE Transactions on Industry Applications*, Nov./Dec. 1981.

[22] Morley, L. A. *Mine Power Systems*, IC9258. Wash., DC: U.S. Bureau of Mines, 1990.

[23] Nichols, N. "The Electrical Considerations in Cogeneration." *IEEE Transactions on Industry Applications*, vol. 1A-21, no. 4, May/June 1985.

[24] Prothero, J. N., DeNardo, C. M., and Lukecart, B. W. "Primary Neutral-to-Earth Voltage Levels as Affected by System Grounding, Neutral Separation and Load Balancing," *IEEE IAS Conference Record*, Oct. 1989.

[25] Shipp, D. D. and Nichols, N. "Designing to Avoid Hazardous Transferred Earth Potentials," *IEEE Transactions on Industry Applications*, vol. 1A-18, no. 4, July/Aug. 1982.

[26] Stetson, L. E., Bodman, G. R., and Shull, H. "An Analog Model of Neutral-to-Earth Voltages in a Single Phase Distribution System," *IEEE Transactions on Industry Applications*, vol. IA-20, No. 2, Mar./Apr. 1984.

[27] Surbrook, T. C. and Reese, N. D. "Trouble Shooting Earth to Neutral Voltage," *IEEE IAS Conference Record*, Oct. 1989.

[28] Liebert Corp., "System Grounding for Uninterruptible Power Systems," Pub. SL-PLT-41, *Technical/Application News*.

[29] Zipse, D. W. "Multiple Neutral-to-Ground Connections," *IEEE I&CPS Technical Conference*, May 1972, pp. 60–64.

1.13 Bibliography

ANSI C2-1990, National Electrical Safety Code.

IEEE Std 242-1986 (Reaffirmed 1991), IEEE Recommended Practice for Protection and Coordination of Industrial and Commercial Power Systems (IEEE Buff Book) (ANSI).

Baker, D. S. "Charging Current Data for Guesswork-Free Design of High Resistance Grounded Systems," *IEEE Transactions on Industry Applications*, vol. IA-15, No. 2, pp. 13:6-140, Mar./Apr. 1979.

Bridger, B. Jr. "High Resistance Grounding," *IEEE Transactions on Industry Applications*, vol. IA-19, no. 2, Jan/Feb 1983, pp. 15–21.

Castenschiold, R. "Grounding of Alternate Power Sources," IEEE Conference Record 77 CHG 1246-B-.IA, Oct. 1977, pp. 92–99.

Gustafson, R. J., and Albertson, V. D. "Neutral-to-Earth Voltage and Ground Current Effects in Livestock Facilities," *IEEE Transactions*, vol. PAS-10, no. 7, July 1982, p. 2090.

Kaufmann, R. H. and Page, J. C. "Arcing Fault Protection for Low-Voltage Power Distribution Systems," *AIEE Transactions on Power Apparatus and Systems*, vol. 79, June 1960, pp. 160–167.

Surbrook, T. R., Reese, N. D. and Althouse, J. R., "Parameters Affecting Neutral-to-Earth Voltage Along Primary Distribution Circuits," *IEEE Transactions on Industry Applications*, vol. 24, no. 5, Sep./Oct. 1988.

Wagner, C. L. "Effect of Grounding Impedance on the Magnitude of Transient Overvoltage Due to Arcing Grounds," *Electric Utility Engineering Report*, no. 60–166, Westinghouse Electric Corp., June 14, 1960.

Wagner, C. L., Ferguson, W. H., and Nordman, D. A. "High Resistance Grounding for Unit-Connected Generators," *Electric Utility Engineering Report*, no. 59–58, Westinghouse Electric Corp., Feb. 27, 1959.

Chapter 2

Equipment Grounding

2.1 Basic Objectives

2.1.1 General

The term *equipment grounding* refers to the interconnection and grounding of the nonelectrical metallic elements of a system. Examples of components of the equipment-grounding system are metallic conduit, motor frames, equipment enclosures, and a grounding conductor. Note that a *grounding conductor* is a part of the equipment grounding system, as distinguished from a *grounded conductor*, which is a part of the power distribution system. The basic objectives of an equipment-grounding system are the following:

1) To reduce electric shock hazard to personnel.
2) To provide adequate current carrying capability, both in magnitude and duration, to accept the ground-fault current permitted by the overcurrent protection system without creating a fire or explosive hazard to building or contents.
3) To provide a low impedance return path for ground-fault current necessary for the timely operation of the overcurrent protection system.

2.1.2 Electric-Shock Exposure

Electric shock injuries result from contact with metallic components that are unintentionally energized [10].[7] Effective equipment grounding practices can minimize these personal injuries.

A breakdown of insulation can cause accidental contact between an energized electrical conductor and the metal frame that encloses it. Such contact tends to energize the frame to the voltage level of the conductor. Avoiding shock-hazard voltage requires nullifying this tendency. The equipment-grounding system should do this by forming a low impedance path to ground.

The impedance of the grounding conductor must be low enough to accept the available line-to-ground-fault current without creating a hazardous impedance *(IZ)* voltage drop. The available ground-fault current of the supply system will have a direct bearing on the equipment-grounding conductor requirements.

2.1.3 Thermal Capability

The grounding conductor must also function to conduct the available ground-fault current (magnitude and duration) without excessive temperature rise or arcing. The use of a large cross-section grounding conductor is not enough. All parts of the fault circuit, including the terminations and other parts, must be capable of carrying the fault current without distress. The installation must also provide a lower impedance fault return path than other possible parallel paths that may have inadequate current-carrying capacity.

Summaries of large-loss fires indicate that approximately one out of four fires in manufacturing establishments originates in electrical systems (see Reference [19]). These reports undoubtedly place some unjustified blame on electrical systems. Effective design, installation, and maintenance of equipment-grounding systems is a vital element in reducing these fire hazards.

---

[7]The numbers in brackets correspond to those of the references in 2.10.

Joints and connectors are critical components of the fault return path. Good workmanship is essential to a safe system and must be demanded. Supervision of installation, inspection, and proper maintenance should assure that the grounding system is not compromised.

One of the more critical connections is the locknut connection between metallic raceway or cable and the sheet metal enclosure. Particular assurance that this connection be made and maintained clean and tight is imperative. A grounding bushing, as required by ANSI/NFPA 70-1990 (the NEC) [1] for services and systems of over 250 V to ground, with its terminal bonded to an adequate terminal within the enclosure, is recommended for all applications.

2.1.4 Overcurrent Protection Operation

The equipment-ground system is an essential part of the overcurrent protection system. The overcurrent protection system requires a low-impedance ground return path in order to operate promptly and properly (see Reference [1], Section 110-10). The earth ground system is rarely of low enough impedance and is not intended to provide an adequate return path. The impedance of the grounding conductor must be low enough that sufficient ground-fault current will flow to operate the overcurrent protective device and clear the fault rapidly.

In ac applications, it is the total impedance $(R+jX)$ that controls the current division among paralleled paths. In 60 Hz circuits rated 40 A or less, the circuit reactance (jX) is an insignificant part of the circuit impedance. Because reactance increases significantly with conductor separation, reactance is the predominant element of impedance for open wire and tray systems for circuits rated above 200 A (see Fig 28). For cable systems or conductors in conduit with close proximity, reactance is a significant component of impedance for circuits rated over 200 A. The reactance of an ac circuit is determined mainly by the spacing between outgoing and return conductors and is only slightly affected by conductor size (see Fig 28). The circuit resistance is directly affected by conductor size. This means that the ratio of X/R and the relative effect of reactance on circuit impedance increases as the conductor size increases.

NOTE — Increased separation spacing between grounding and phase conductors increases not only the reactance X_g of the grounding conductor but also the zero-sequence reactance X_0 of the phase conductors.

In 60 Hz ac circuits rated above 40 A, it becomes mandatory that the installed grounding conductor be physically placed to present a much lower reactance than other less capable parallel paths. The manner in which this is achieved is treated in 2.2.

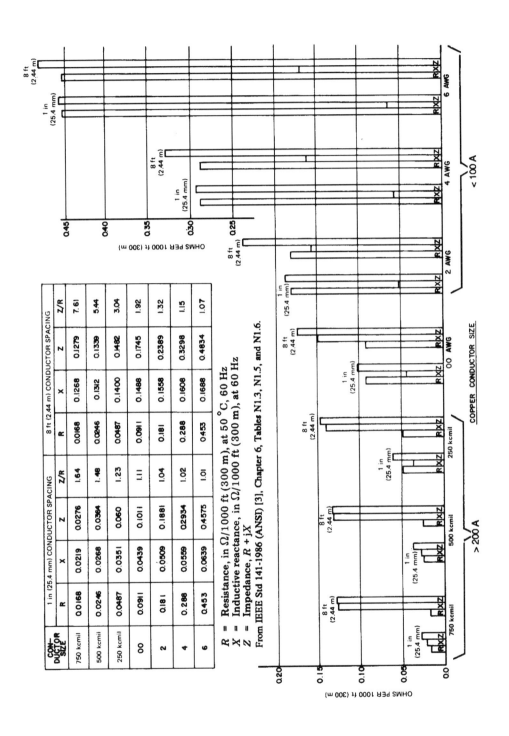

Figure 28—Variation of *R* and *X* with Conductor Size and Spacing

2.2 Fundamental Concepts

2.2.1 A Single Wire as a Grounding Conductor

To help develop an understanding of the behavior pattern of a single wire as a grounding conductor, see Fig 29. (For an expanded treatment of single line-to-ground fault behavior, see Reference [14].)

The grounding conductor is considered to be bonded to the supply system grounded conductor, to the building frame, and to the grounding electrode at the source end of the circuit. For the purpose of examining the properties of the grounding conductor alone, it will be considered to be installed in metallic conduit and to remain free of any other contact with the building frame throughout its length of 200 ft (61 m). Imagine the circuit to be of 350 A capacity, employing 500 kcmil (253.35 mm^2) phase conductors and a 4/0 (107.16 mm^2) grounding conductor (copper) at 25 °C. It is assumed that the line-to-ground fault current at the outer terminal is 5500 A.

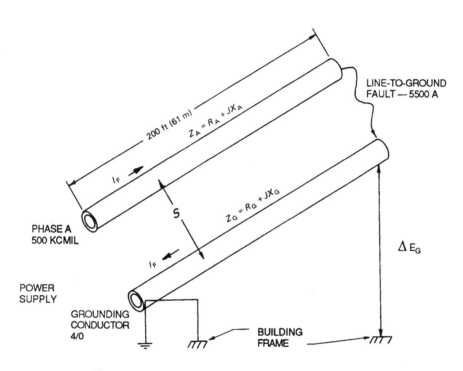

Figure 29—Single Wire as Grounding Conductor

Consideration will be given to three values of spacing between phase and grounding conductors: 2, 8, and 30 in (51, 203, and 762 mm). The 60 Hz impedance values for phase and grounding conductors at 50 °C in ohms for the 200 ft (61 m) run are as follows (see Reference [3], Tables N1.3 and N1.5, Chapter 6):

Table 1—Impedance as a Function of Conductor Spacing

	Spacing (in)	Spacing (mm)	R	X (j)	Z
Phase conductor A	2	51	0.0049	0.0085	0.0098
	8	203	0.0049	0.0149	0.0157
	30	762	0.0049	0.0210	0.0216
Grounding conductor G	2	51	0.0115	0.0108	0.0158
	8	203	0.0115	0.0172	0.0207
	30	762	0.0115	0.0233	0.0260

In Fig 29, the $I_F Z_G$ voltage drop along the grounding conductor appears as a touch electric shock at the far end of the grounding conductor. At the presumed ground-fault current I_F of 5500 A, the magnitude of shock-voltage exposure for each of the three spacings is shown in Table 2.

Table 2—Shock Voltage as a Function of Conductor Spacing

Spacing (in)	Spacing (mm)	E_G (V)
2	51	86.9
8	203	113.9
30	762	143.0

The change in spacing also changes the reactance of the phase conductor (relative to the grounding conductor). The corresponding values of the phase-conductor voltage drop (I_F held constant at 5500 A) are shown in Table 3.

Table 3—Phase Conductor Voltage Drop

Spacing (in)	Spacing (mm)	IZ Drop, Phase A (V)
2	51	53.9
8	203	86.4
30	762	118.8

A change in the location of the grounding conductor changes the value of the reactance in the phase conductor. This fact leads directly to the next important concept. While our impedance diagrams display both resistance and reactance as properties of the conductor, the reactance is, in fact, a property of the space electromagnetic field which encircles the conductor. For the conductor geometry shown in Fig 29, the magnetic field, which is responsible for the reactive voltage drop, assumes the character shown in Fig 30. Throughout the space between the two conductors (8 in [203 mm] wide and 200 ft [61 m] long) exists a powerful 60 Hz magnetic field with a driving magnetomotive force of 5500 A turns. It constitutes a huge electromagnet. That portion of the total magnetic field that encircles the grounding conductor is considered to be associated with the reactance of the grounding conductor, while that which encircles the phase conductor is considered to be associated with the reactance of the phase conductor.

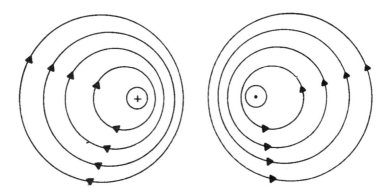

Figure 30—Magnetic Field of Wire as Grounding Conductor

Any loop of conducting material (wire, pipe, messenger cable, steel structure, etc.) through which some fractional portion of this magnetic field passes will have induced in it a corresponding fractional part of the 60 Hz reactive voltage drop of the main power circuit loop. There need be no physical contact between the two loops. The mutual coupling is entirely magnetic. If the loop in which the voltage is mutually coupled is closed, then instead of a voltage, a circulating current will exist.

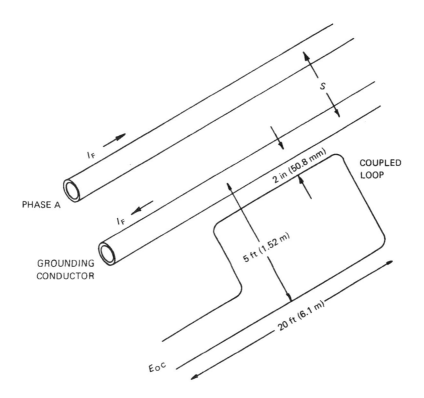

Figure 31—Electromagnetic Induction of Wire as Grounding Conductor

Figure 31 shows a possible loop alongside the grounding conductor (not the most intensive field strength location). With this loop considered to be open at one corner, the generated voltage therein would be 1.65 V for a 2 in (51 mm) grounding-conductor spacing, or 5.61 V for a 30 in (762 mm) spacing. If the loop circuit is closed, the flux linkages through this loop will be reduced to near zero, and the induced current will assume the value that becomes necessary to oppose the entrance of flux linkages. In the case illustrated, the induced current might very well be of the order of 500 A.

The situation presented by Fig 31 would not be judged to be a dangerous shock voltage exposure, but the possible arcing and flashing that could occur at a light pressure contact point closing the loop (open-circuit voltage of 2–5 V with a closed-circuit current of 500 A) could be a very real source of ignition of combustible material (fire) or of flammable gas (explosion). The same size induction loop around a high capacity outdoor station, where the ground-fault current might be 50 000 A and the spacing between phase and grounding conductors 6 ft (1.83 m), might well display an open circuit 60 Hz induced voltage of dangerous shock-hazard magnitude.

By constructing a closed loop with no loose connections, so positioned as to block the passage of flux linkages responsible for an objectionable reactance, that reactance can be eliminated. As an example, consider a temporary high current ac circuit that is required to pass through a heavy wall via embedded steel pipes. The conductors are too large to be pulled through one piece, so each is pulled through an independent pipe cell. Under load, the voltage drop is excessive, and the pipe sleeves become very hot.

One verdict could be that the installation is unusable. However, with the knowledge just developed we can form a short-circuiting loop that will remove the unwanted reactance and eliminate the steel pipe sleeve heating. Thread bare copper cable around the pipe sleeve loop, out through one pipe and back through the other, continuing until the total cross section that has been threaded through each pipe will carry the full load current. Then close this loop on itself by joining the ends of the cable. Close the power switch and proceed. The circuit reactance will be less than if the main conductors had been in air all the way. There will be a small extra resistance accounted for by the circulating current flowing in the short-circuited loop. This example is intended to convey the principle of the relationship between reactance and flux linkages and is not intended to represent a recommended or even desirable practice.

As far as the shock exposure voltage drop along the grounding conductor is concerned, the key factors are grounding conductor cross-section area, spacing relative to phase conductors, magnitude of ground-fault current, and circuit length.

In the usual installation, the grounding conductor is bonded to the building structure at regular intervals. The first impression is that such bonding causes the shock-exposure voltage to disappear. The correct explanation is that the voltage, which was observed to exist on the grounding conductor, has been impressed on the building structure. At the point of bonding, the potential difference has been reduced to zero. At the service equipment a bonding jumper establishes zero potential difference. Therefore, the voltage drop along the building structure now equals the voltage drop along the grounding conductor because the two paths are in parallel. Perhaps voltage differences have been forced to appear between certain building structural members that are more serious than the original one. The problems of determining what voltage differences will appear between designated points of the building have become considerably more complex. A rational approach to the problem begins with an evaluation of the voltage exposure that would exist with the grounding conductor acting alone. This serves to establish the relative performance quality of the design being studied. It also identifies the maximum voltage difference that could possibly be imparted to the building structure by cross bonding.

Of course, a bonding connection from a grounding conductor to the building frame does result in some drop in the voltage magnitude along the grounding conductor. This drop can become substantial with the smaller rated circuits. An analytical approach to a solution of this problem is contained in Reference [15].

2.2.2 Cabling of Conductors

By cabling or lacing together all the conductors of one circuit, the spacing between grounding and phase conductors can be reduced to the point of direct contact of the insulation. With other conditions remaining as indicated in Fig 29, the 60 Hz reactances could be reduced to 0.0061 Ω for the grounding conductor and to 0.0038 Ω for the phase conductor. While the grounding conductor impedance shows little improvement because it is largely resistance limited, the space magnetic field has been substantially reduced, with a corresponding reduction in magnetic coupling to secondary loop circuits.

By distributing the total grounding conductor cross section among the interstices of a three-conductor cable (one-third size conductor in each pocket), the effective reactance of the grounding conductor can be further reduced, resulting in a corresponding reduction in the space magnetic field strength.

2.2.3 Enclosing Metal Shell

By forming the metal of the grounding conductor into a tubular shape, within which are run the circuit phase and neutral conductors, a marked improvement in effectiveness is accomplished. The returning ground-fault current distributes itself about the entire enclosing shell in such fashion as to result in a lower round-trip voltage drop (see Fig 32). The electrical behavior during a line-to-ground fault is that of a coaxial line. Except for the effects of resistivity in the shell, all electric and magnetic fields are contained inside the shell. The external space magnetic field becomes zero (see Reference [16]).

The customary metal conductor raceway fits this preferred conductor geometry perfectly. It is important that these tubular shaped sections be adequately joined and terminated so that significant additional impedance is not introduced. The normal tubular metal raceway is permitted to serve as the grounding conductor. See NEC, Reference [1], Article 250.

Practical varieties of metal conductor raceways and metal sheathing possess substantial sheath resistance. The flow of ground-fault current will thus produce a voltage gradient along the grounding conductor due to impedance voltage drop. The magnitude of this voltage drop varies widely from one type of grounding method to another. Because of its importance in fixing the magnitude of electric-shock-voltage exposure, a rather extensive array of tests was conducted to provide specific data, and the results are reported in consolidated form in Reference [15]. A variety of grounding conductor types were examined, covering a range of phase-conductor sizes from AWG 12 (3.31 mm^2) to 500 kcmil (253.35 mm^2). The results are presented in terms of voltage drop along the exterior surface per 1000 A of ground-fault current per 100 ft (30.5 m) of circuit length. The published data (see Reference [15], Fig 6, and Table III) is consolidated in Table 4.

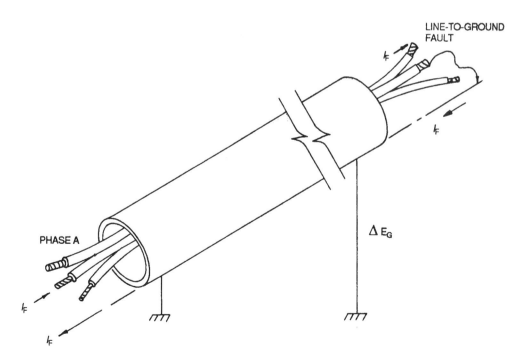

Figure 32—Tubular Metal Raceway as Grounding Conductor

IEEE RECOMMENDED PRACTICE FOR GROUNDING OF

Table 4—Voltage Drop of Conductors in Cable or Conduit

Conductor Size	Cable or Conduit	DC Resistance Ω/100 ft	Computed IR Drop V/1000 A/ 100 ft	*Measured Drop V/1000 A/ 100 ft
500 kcmil	3/C VCI (steel armor)	0.0383	38.3	35
500 kcmil	3/C VCI (steel armor with internal grounding conductor)	—	—	5
#4/0	3/C VCI (aluminum armor)	0.286	286.0	151
#4/0	3/C VCI (aluminum armor with internal grounding conductor)	—	—	12
#4/0	3/C VCI (steel armor)	—	—	55
#4/0	3/C VCI (steel armor with internal grounding conductor)	—	—	11
#4/0	3/C lead sheath (15 kV)	0.00283	2.83	11
#4/0	4" rigid steel conduit	0.0025	2.5	1
#2/0	2" rigid steel conduit	0.0095	9.5	6
#1/0	3/C VCI (steel armor)	0.0458	45.8	51
#1/0	3/C VCI (steel armor with internal grounding conductor)	—	—	19
#2	aluminum sheath (solid sheath M/C cable	0.01	10.0	9
#2	1 1/4" rigid steel	0.0108	10.8	11
#2	1 1/4" EMT	0.0205	20.5	22
#2	1 1/4" Greenfield (flexible metal conduit)	0.435	435.0	436
#8	3/4" rigid steel	0.02	20.0	21
#8	3/4" EMT	0.0517	51.7	48
#8	3/4" greenfield (flexible metal conduit)	1.28	1280.0	1000
#10	aluminum sheath (solid sheath MC Cable)	0.015	15.0	16
#12	1/2" rigid steel	0.0223	22.3	25
#12	1/2" EMT	0.0706	70.6	70
#12	BX without ground (AC cable)	1.79[†]	1790.0	1543

*Value read from bar chart (numeric values not published).
†Does not meet current Underwriters Laboratories' listing requirements.

Rigid steel conduit is observed to offer superior performance, principally because of the heavy wall thickness. The striking contrast between steel and aluminum conduit is interesting and offers specific application advantages. The high magnetic permeability of steel should and does account for a higher line- to-ground fault impedance (see References [6], [15], and [16]). It would at first seem that the voltage drop along the raceway exterior would also be increased, yet the exact opposite is observed. The effect of the magnetic material in the conduit wall is to confine the return current largely to the internal shell of the conduit, penetrating to the exterior surface only as magnetic saturation in the iron occurs for large fault currents.

It should be noted that the values listed in Table 4 for Greenfield (flexible metal conduit) and BX without ground (AC cable) are excessive for the armor to be used as an equipment-grounding conductor. Current standards require that BX incorporate an internal bonding strip in contact with the metal armor over the full length. The NEC, Reference [1], requires a separate equipment grounding conductor in Greenfield except for very short sections.

It is significant to note the sharp decrease in voltage drop when an internal grounding conductor is added in parallel with the conduit. In addition, the line-to-ground fault impedance will be reduced. Thus, the use of a metallic conduit raceway as a grounding conductor, supplemented by an equipment-grounding conductor within the conduit, achieves both minimum ground fault impedance (see Reference [9]) and minimum shock-hazard voltage.

The NEC [1] provides no specific limitations on the length of tubular metal raceway or cable armor that may be used as an equipment-grounding conductor. It is apparent, though, that excessive length can result in an impedance that will limit the ability of the circuit overcurrent device to clear a ground fault as well as cause a hazardous voltage on the raceway or cable armor surface. Reference [21] contains some examples of maximum lengths as a function of overcurrent device rating. The resulting reduction of impedance when an internal grounding conductor is added in parallel with a metal raceway will permit feeder distance to be increased by up to 1.7 times the maximum feeder length without the internal conductor.

For the circuit arrangement indicated in Fig 29, the progressive improvement in shock voltage exposure with different forms of grounding conductors is displayed in Table 5. (The conditions of Fig 29 are maintained, except for grounding conductor size and shape. I_F is held constant at 5500 A. The 30 in (762 ram) spacing is included only for reference. This spacing is unlikely in most industrial applications.)

Making the grounding conductor a conduit enclosing the phase conductor, the shock-voltage exposure E_g drops to 6.7 V for rigid aluminum conduit and to 11 V for rigid steel conduit.

The effective performance of an enclosing raceway as a grounding conductor should be used to full advantage in electrical system designs. It is important to avoid the use of raceways having inadequate short-time current-carrying capacity unless supplemented with an adequate additional equipment-grounding conductor run within the raceway. Joints between raceway sections and other grounding connections must provide good electrical conduction at high fault current levels or the effectiveness of the raceway as a grounding path will be lost. The value of good workmanship cannot be overestimated.

Reported in the literature (see References [9] and [16]), but not documented in detail, is the fact that, where more than a single length of conduit was used for a ground return path, sparks were observed at conduit junctions and connections to boxes at the beginning of the experimental measurements. The sparking did not occur during subsequent tests because either the conduit connections were made more secure or the conduit sections welded to each other by the resultant electrical arcs. This is in substantial agreement with observations made by many field engineers but not substantiated in current technical literature.

Table 5—Shock Voltage as a Function of Conductor

Grounding Conductor	Shock-Voltage Exposure Eg (V)
#4/0 (107.16 mm^2) copper with 30 in (762 mm) spacing	151.3
#4/0(107.16 mm^2) copper with 8 in (203 mm) spacing	124.3
#4/0 (107.16 mm^2) copper with 2 in (51 mm) spacing	100.1
Triple ground wires, #4/0 (107.16 mm^2) total in three-conductor cable	70.4

2.2.4 Circuit Impedance Components

The general expression for the three phase line-to-ground-fault current in a three phase system is

$$I_F = \frac{3E_A}{Z_1 + Z_2 + Z_0 + 3Z_G} \tag{2}$$

Both positive-sequence (Z_1) and negative- sequence (Z_2) impedance are active only in the outgoing phase conductors since the currents of these two sequences combine to zero at the fault location. The zero-sequence currents I_0, however, are in phase on all phase conductors. Three of the phase conductor currents I_0 must be returned collectively ($3I_0$) over the grounding conductor. Thus the transit of the zero-sequence current involves a voltage drop of I_0Z_0 in transmitting the current out over the phase conductors and a voltage drop of $3I_0Z_G$ in transmitting the current back over the grounding conductor. A correct accounting of impedance for these two terms in the zero-sequence network develops when I_0 is taken out as one factor [$I_0 (Z_0 + 3Z_G)$].

Test results [6], [9], [15], and [16] clearly display the fact that the round-trip impedance ($Z_0 + 3Z_G$) is much greater than Z_0, yet the fractional part of the round-trip zero-sequence voltage drop, which appears along the raceway exterior, is but a very small part of $I_0(Z_0 + 3Z_G)$. No easy way to separate Z_0 from $3Z_G$ is available, and in fact no purpose is served in separating them. It is very important to recognize that both items are present and that the use of the circuit Z_0 alone would represent a gross error.

As can be seen from [15], the ($Z_0 + 3Z_0$)/Z_1 ratio can be kept low, leading to a low-impedance (Z_G) ground return path. This is obtained by using ground conductors or buses, or both, in conduit runs, cables, busway and equipment.

It is often erroneously concluded that multiple connection of the ground return path to building steel has only positive results. The benefits are:

1) no voltage hazard is present at the location where the building steel is connected, and
2) an alternate return path exists in the event that there is a break in the intended return path.

However, the following potential disadvantage may exist:

1) Diversion of ground return current through building steel may cause sparking at structural steel joints not intended to be electrically conductive.
2) Return current that is not near to the faulted phase conductor will increase the reactance of the phase conductor and the return path.
3) Fault voltage will be applied to the building structure and, if not uniformly distributed due to high impedance joints, may result in hazardous touch potentials.

2.2.5 Electromagnetic Interference Suppression

In developing the fundamental behavior patterns of the various forms of grounding conductors, the ability to suppress the magnitude of the electric and magnetic fields in the space external to the electric power channel by proper design methods was noted. This knowledge can be employed to make the grounding conductor serve to significantly reduce the electrical noise contributed to the space surrounding the electrical run. As might be expected from results so far defined, the enclosing metal raceway is superior to discrete conductors. Tubular steel raceways are very effective in suppressing strong fields. High conductance may be needed to achieve very low noise levels.

The rapidly increasing use of low energy level digital data transmission circuits in combination with a fast growing noise level on power circuit conductors due to time modulation current choppers, usually SCRs (silicon controlled rectifiers), for accomplishing heating appliance control, light-circuit dimming, motor-speed control, etc., emphasizes the importance of this electromagnetic interference suppression function (see References [11], [12], [20], and [23]).

2.2.6 Bonding of Metal Sleeves Enclosing a Grounding Conductor

The behavior pattern of an independent grounding conductor (such as the run to the grounding electrode at the service or the grounding conductor connecting a surge arrestor to an earthing terminal) is very different from that of a power circuit grounding conductor (see Fig 33).

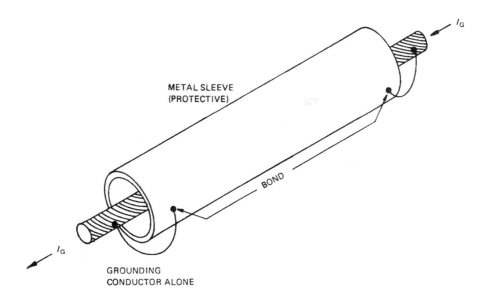

METAL SLEEVE (PROTECTIVE)

BOND

I_G

I_G

GROUNDING CONDUCTOR ALONE

Figure 33—Bonding of Metal Enclosure

The function in this case is to conduct the one-way current to a grounding (earthing) electrode. The return path of this current is remote from the grounding conductor. In the case of lightning current, the return path may be so remote as to be obscure. There will be an inductive voltage drop along the conductor length due to a changing current ($L \cdot di/dt$ or $X_L \cdot I_{ac}$). The larger the conductor diameter, the lower will be the conductor inductance (or reactance). If the member enclosing the conductor is magnetic, the magnetic field encircling the conductor is increased, which correspondingly increases the inductive voltage drop. If the enclosure is plastic conduit, there will not be a magnetic effect.

An inductance is commonly made by wrapping a number of turns of conductor wire around a magnetic (iron) core. An equally effective method is to "wrap" a magnetic (iron) cylinder around a conductor. Such a cylinder is a steel conduit, although even aluminum has an effect from eddy current generated in the conduit. It has been found that enclosing a single grounding conductor in steel conduit increases its impedance by a factor of up to 40.

In some cases, installation conditions are such as to warrant the application of a metal enclosure over a section of this type of grounding conductor. In all cases where this is done, *the conductor and the enclosing protective metal shell should be bonded together at both ends of every integral section of enclosure* for the following reasons:

1)   To avoid increased voltage drop if the enclosure is made of magnetic material.
2)   To take advantage of the lower voltage drop associated with larger conductor diameter (see Reference [6] for complete details).
3)   To permit the steel conduit to carry the major portion of the ground seeking current.

2.2.7 Grounding Connections Associated with Steep Wave Front Voltage Protection Equipment

The application of surge arresters to transformers (see Fig 34) and surge protective capacitors and arrestors to rotating machines (see Fig 35) illustrate this application of a grounding conductor. The function of the grounding conductor is to provide a conducting path over which the surge current can be diverted around the apparatus being protected, without developing a dangerous voltage magnitude.

In the presence of a changing current (di/dt) there will be an inductive voltage drop developed along the grounding conductor itself, which is additive to the protective device voltage. The amount of this added voltage will be proportion to the conductor length and the spacing from the protected apparatus and of course to the magnitude of di/dt.

Actual values of di/dt range over wide limits, but a value of 10 kA/μs is representative. With such a rate of rise of current, even 1 μH tall of inductance can be significant.

$$E = L \cdot di/dt \qquad\qquad\qquad (3)$$
$$= 10^{-6} \cdot 10\ 000 \cdot 10^{6}$$
$$= 10\ 000\ \text{V}$$

NOTE — μH is the equivalent of 0.000377 Ω reactance at 60 Hz.

It would take only a 3 ft (0.91 m) length of AWG 4/0 (107.16 mm^2) conductor spaced 5 ft (1.52 m) away from the transformer in Fig 34 to add 10 000 V to the arrestor voltage. Thus, grounding conductor length and spacing become of paramount importance. One can readily visualize that the additive inductive voltage is generated by the total flux linkages that can be developed through the window between the grounding conductor and the protected apparatus.

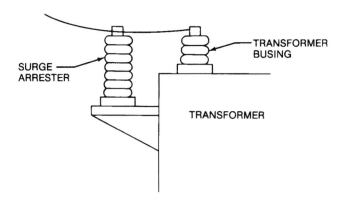

Figure 34—Surge Arrester Location on Transformer

To take full advantage of the protective properties of the surge arrester in Fig 34, the arrester should be mounted so as to be in direct shunt relationship to the terminal bushings. At lower voltages an arrester supporting bracket can usually be extended from the base of the bushing. At higher voltages a shelf extending from the tank body at the proper place to minimize the inductive voltage is often used to support the arresters.

Locating the arrestor at any substantial distance, such as at the poletop crossarm, with an independent grounding conductor can seriously increase the surge voltage stress on a transformer or switchgear by the voltage drop in the arrestor down lead to ground. Arresters should be as close as possible to the equipment to be protected and to ground.

The same fundamental reasoning applies to the installation geometry of rotating machine surge-protective equipment (see Fig 35). A box, shelf, or bracket directly adjacent to the emerging leads from the machine can accomplish the desired objective. The mounting frame should connect directly with the machine frame to minimize the circuit inductance. It is the capacitor element of the protection system that deserves prime attention. If this item is properly connected with short, direct connecting leads, the rate of rise of voltage at the motor terminal will be quite gentle, requiring perhaps 10 µs to build up to arrester sparkover value. Thus the leads to the arrester can be longer because of the modest rate of rise of voltage. In fact, there can be a benefit from inductance in the arrester circuit, which cushions the abrupt drop in machine terminal voltage when the arrester sparks over.

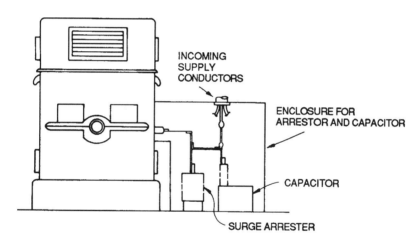

Figure 35—Surge Protection Equipment on Motor*
***Only One Phase Shown for Clarity**

2.2.8 Connection to Earth

(See Chapter 4 for more details.) The well-established usage of the terms *ground* and *earth* in our technical literature leads to many misconceptions, since they seemingly are almost alike, yet in fact are not. The electrical system of an aircraft in flight will have a ground bus, grounding conductors, etc. To suggest that ground and earth can be used interchangeably is obviously in error here. To an electrician working on the tenth floor of a modern steel-structured building, the referenced ground is the building frame, attached metal equipment, and the family of electrical system grounding conductors present at the working area. What might be the potential of earth is of negligible importance to this worker on the tenth floor.

If the worker is transported to the building basement in which the concrete floor slab rests on soil, or to the yard area of an outdoor open-frame substation, earth does become the proper reference ground to which electric shock voltage exposure should be referenced.

Thus, the proper reference ground to be used in expressing voltage exposure magnitudes may sometimes be earth, but (outside of the outdoor substation area) most likely will be the electric circuit metallic grounding conductor. The following paragraphs will show that the potential of earth may be greatly different from that of the grounding conductor. It therefore becomes very important that shock-exposure voltages be expressed relative to the proper reference ground.

All electrical systems, even those installed in airborne vehicles (as at least one Apollo crew can testify), may be faced with circumstances in which sources of electric current are seeking a path to ground. These conditions can do serious damage to electrical equipment or develop dangerous electric-shock-hazard exposure to persons in the area, unless this stray current is diverted to a preplanned path to a ground of adequate capability.

A comprehensive treatment of the behavior of earthing terminals appears in Chapter 4 and in References [2], [4], [7], and [22]. The prime purpose of this discussion is to develop a concept of the potential gradients created in discharging current into earth and the manner in which the equipment grounding problem is influenced thereby.

Earth is inherently a rather poor conductor whose resistivity is around one billion times that of copper. A 10 ft (3 m) long by 5/8 in (16 mm) diameter ground rod driven into earth might very likely represent a 25 Ω connection to earth. This resistance may be imagined to be made up of the collective resistance of a series of equal thickness concentric cylindrical shells of earth. The inner shell will of course represent the largest incremental value of resistance, since the resistance is inversely proportion to the shell diameter. Thus the central small diameter shells of earth constitute the bulk of the earthing terminal resistance. Half of the 25 Ω resistance value would likely be contained within a 1 ft (0.15 m) diameter cylinder (see 4.1.1).

For the same reason, half of the voltage drop resulting from current injection into this grounding electrode would appear across the first 0.5 ft (0.15 m) of earth surface radially away from the ground rod. If a current of 1000 A were forced into this grounding electrode, the rod would be forced to rise above mean earth potential by 25 000 V (1000 · 25). Half of this voltage (12 500 V) would appear as a voltage drop between the rod and the earth spaced only 0.5 ft (0.15 m) away from the rod. While this current is flowing, a person standing on earth 0.5 ft (0.15 m) away from the ground rod and touching the connecting lead to the electrode would be spanning a potential difference of 12 500 V. A three-dimensional plot of earth surface potential versus distance from the ground rod would create the anthill-shape displayed in Fig 36. The central peak value would be the rod potential (referred to remote earth potential), namely, 25 000 V. Moving away from the rod in any horizontal direction would rapidly reduce the voltage value. The half-voltage contour would be a horizontal circle 1 ft (0.3 m) in diameter encircling the rod.

Imagine a 50 by 50 ft (15.2 by 15.2 m) substation area within which 25 driven rods, each of the type previously described, had been uniformly distributed. Because of the overlapping potential gradient patterns, the composite resistance will not be as low as 25/25 Ω. For the case at hand, a 2 Ω value would be typical (see Chapter 4). Should a line-to-ground fault at this station produce a 10 000 A discharge into the earthing terminal, the resulting voltage contour map would display 25 sharp-pointed potential mounds peaking at 20 000 V. In between would be dish-shaped voltage contours with minimum values ranging from perhaps 2000 to 5000 V, depending on location.

Such a highly variable voltage contour pattern within the walking area of the substation would not be acceptable. Additional shallow buried grounding wires can be employed to elevate the earth surface potential between main electrodes (see Reference [2]). Note particularly the concepts of step, touch, and transferred potentials. Additional shallow buried grounding wires can be employed to tailor the voltage contour adjacent to but external to the enclosing fence. Beds of coarse cracked rock, well drained to prevent standing water, can contribute to improved electric shock security. Metal grill mats bonded to the steel-framework supporting switch operating handles and located at the "standing" location of switch operators can ensure that the operator's hands and feet are referenced to the same potential.

2.3 Equipment Grounding as Influenced by Type of Use

The principal classes of use may be categorized for our purposes as follows:

1) outdoor open frame substations

2)   outdoor unit substations
3)   outdoor portable heavy duty equipment, such as shovels, draglines, dredges
4)   interior wiring systems
5)   interior substations and switching centers

The problems presented to the equipment-grounding system designer vary quite widely with the different classes of use. The basic objectives remain the same throughout. The equipment-grounding system must cope with the current flow (magnitude and duration) that is imposed on it by extraordinary events which occur during the course of ordinary power-system operation. This duty is most commonly the result of an insulation failure between an energized conductor and the conductive metallic structure that supports or encloses it. However, the duty may result from an outside injection of current, such as a lightning discharge or a falling overhead high-voltage conductor. The equipment-grounding system is expected to carry this imposed current without thermal distress and without creating dangerous electric-shock-voltage exposure to persons in the area.

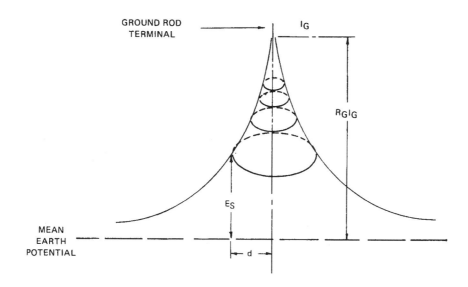

E_s = EARTH SURFACE POTENTIAL
d = RADIAL DISTANCE FROM ROD
R_g = RESISTANCE OF ROD TO EARTH
I_g = GROUND CURRENTS INTO ROD

Figure 36—Earth Surface Potential Around Ground Rod During Current Flow
(See Table 9, Chapter 4)

2.4 Outdoor Open Frame Substations

2.4.1 General

The distributed nature of the typical outdoor open-frame substation (see Fig 37) presents some of the most perplexing equipment grounding problems to be found anywhere. It is quite common that various pieces of major apparatus will appear as "island" installations within the substation area. For any single equipment item, the voltage stress imposed on its insulation system will be determined by the voltage difference between its electrical terminals and the frame or metal case which encloses its active parts. The magnitude of electric-shock exposure to an operating or maintenance person within the substation area proper will be a function of the voltage difference between the ground surface on which this person stands and the metal that the person normally touches, such as apparatus frames or substation structure (see Reference [2]). The magnitude of electric-shock-voltage exposure to a person approaching the enclosing fence will depend on the character of the earth surface voltage gradient contours adjacent to the fence on the outside of the substation area.

Figure 37—Open-Frame Outdoor Substation Showing Lightning Masts, Surge Arresters, and Low-Voltage Side Grounding Resistors

2.4.2 Design of Avenues for Power Frequency Ground-Fault Current Flow

This ability to carry the ground-fault current from the point where it enters the station to the point where it is to depart is accomplished by supplementing the inherent metallic substation structure with an array of grounding conductors that interconnect the bases of structural columns and are extended to the island installations of apparatus, routed over appropriate paths [6], [16]. Copper cable is generally used for this purpose, with the conductor size ranging from AWG 2/0 (70.1 mm^2) for small stations, for instance, to perhaps 500 kcmil (253.35 mm^2) for large stations. It is appropriate to seek an effective short-time current capability in the grounding conductor path, which is no less than 25% of that possessed by the phase conductor with which it is associated. In any case, it should be capable of accepting the line-to-ground short circuit current (magnitude and duration) permitted to flow by the overcurrent protection system without thermal distress. (See [2] for design equations.)

The routing of a grounding conductor should seek to minimize the separation distance between it and the associated phase conductors. In multibay metal structure construction, the short-circuited loops created by the bonding of grounding conductors between column bases may effectively limit the ground-circuit reactance under seemingly wide spacing conditions.

Grounding conductors sized and routed according to the same rules should be run to those points required for system grounding connections, such as to the neutral terminal of a power transformer that is to be grounded or to the neutral of a grounding transformer.

Junctions between sections of wire grounding conductors should be made by exothermic welding or brazing (Fig 38). At the terminations, exothermic welding, brazing, or fittings approved for the purpose should be used.

Figure 38—Thermal-Weld Junction in Underground Grounding Conductor

If overhead-line ground conductors are terminated at towers along the substation outer boundary and the phase conductors continue out across the station plot, perhaps to a point where they drop down to apparatus terminals, an adequately sized grounding conductor should be strung across the area with a vertical down member to the apparatus frame to establish a path for ground current flow that remains reasonably close to the route of the phase conductors.

It is important that the grounding conductor system extend to and connect with each of the island structures contained within the substation area.

2.4.3 Design of Earthing Connections

The achievement of a prescribed degree of connection to earth will constitute an important design objective. This usually will involve a multiplicity of earthing connections (grounding electrodes) distributed about the substation area. If individual grounding electrodes are not kept sufficiently separated physically, their effectiveness is severely impaired (see Chapter 4).

One specific design limit may be the maximum allowable voltage excursion on the substation structure (relative to mean earth potential) due to a line-to-ground power system fault or a lightning discharge. All signal and communication circuits that extend from this station to remote locations must be designed to accommodate this voltage excursion without damage. The allowable voltage excursion on the station structure may be limited by the voltage rating of a power circuit entering the station. Consider, for instance, a station whose main circuits operate at 230 kV, but which contains outgoing circuits operating at 4.16 kV. A voltage excursion on the station ground mat of 25 kV would not be troublesome to the 230 kV system, but would be disastrous to components of the 4.16 kV system. Even the best of available surge arresters on the 4.16 kV circuits would be to no avail. The excess seal-off voltage present would promptly result in their destruction. The allowable maximum voltage excursion on the station ground mat may be set by one of a variety of factors. Once this is set, the design of the station grounding connection systems can proceed.

The effectiveness of reinforcing steel located in below-grade foundation footing as functional grounding electrodes is discussed in Reference [18]. All future station design specifications should call for electrical bonding between the metal tower base plate and the reinforcing bars in buried concrete footings. This can be accomplished readily in most instances via the hold-down J bolts, provided that the belts are bonded to the reinforcing bars.

If the soil at the substation site tends to be an active electrolyte like cinder fill, the use of dissimilar metals (for instance, copper and steel) as grounding electrodes bonded together in the station-grounding conductor network may lead to objectionable electrolytic deterioration of the buried steel members (see Reference [8]). With today's knowledge, the avoidance of such trouble may be relatively easy. When the soil is active, with a resistivity less than 2000 Ω-cm, the required earthing connection may be obtained using only the buried steel members forming an inherent part of the station. If the soil is not active, the intermix of metals such as copper and steel is not troublesome.

Lightning masts extending upward from the top structural members of the station can be effective in intercepting lightning strokes and leading the discharged current to earth without insulation flashover at the station. The avoidance of insulation flashover is aided by higher insulation flashover levels at the station and opposed by more intense lightning strokes. However, an installation that reduces the number of flashover incidents by 60% (far short of perfection) can still be a sound economic investment (see Chapter 3).

2.4.4 Surge Voltage Protective Equipment

Surge voltage protective devices intended to deal effectively with fast-front voltage transients must be connected in a close shunt relationship to the apparatus being protected (see 2.2.7).

The presence of an exposed overhead line running to the station, but terminating at an open switch or open circuit breaker, invites a flashover at the open terminal because of the tendency for a traveling voltage wave to double its voltage upon encountering an open terminal. The possibility of such an event and its consequences should receive deliberate consideration. If found to be likely, and objectionable, this type of flashover can be prevented by the installation of line type surge arresters directly ahead of the open circuit point on the circuit or by over insulation (double normal value of the approaching line) of the terminal end of the line within the confines of the station, ahead of the point of open circuit. Both sides of an open switch may need surge arrester protection if there is lightning exposure on both sides.

NOTE — This increased withstand voltage also applies to the circuit-opening switching device.

2.4.5 Control of Surface Voltage Gradient

The tendency for steeply rising voltage gradients to appear directly around discrete grounding electrodes results in a very nonuniform ground surface potential in the substation area during a ground fault incident. This can appear as a dangerous electric shock voltage exposure to the persons working in the substation area (see References [2], [4], [7], and [22]). It is hardly reasonable to design for a maximum voltage excursion on the station structure low enough to avoid danger. The alternative approach is to employ a mesh grid of relatively small bare conductors located slightly below grade and connected to the station frame. Although this will not likely reduce the overall station earthing resistance by very much, it will function (like conducting tape on cable insulation) to bring all parts of the substation surface earth lying above the grid mesh to nearly the same potential as the metal grid (that of the substation metal structure). Only small scallops of lesser voltage magnitude will exist between the crisscross conductors of the grid mesh. The possible magnitude of electric-shock-voltage exposure to maintenance personnel due to earth surface gradients can be reduced to tolerable levels. A surface layer of coarse cracked rock is commonly employed to contribute to reduced contact conductance between the yard surface and the worker's feet.

2.4.6 Voltage Gradients External to but Adjacent to the Boundary Fence

The steepness of the surface voltage contour adjacent to but outside the enclosing fence determines whether a person approaching the fence and touching it to the limit of their reach could receive a dangerous electric shock. If the fence were allowed to float, the adjacent voltage gradient would be substantially reduced. Common practice is to bond the fence to the station ground mat, which will take it up to the full mat potential and create a high surface gradient adjacent to the fence. In defense of the practice of bonding the fence to the station ground mat is the added security afforded should a high voltage line conductor break and fall on the fence. The bond to the station ground allows the entire station grounding connection to participate in holding down the voltage magnitude of the fence and avoiding ground fault impedance that might otherwise impede the performance of ground overcurrent relaying. Operating the enclosing fence at station ground mat potential also improves the uniformity of surface gradient within the substation area.

An inviting alternative would locate the boundary fence along a specific voltage contour line (or design for a constant voltage contour along the desired route of the fence). This approach might easily result in a 50% reduction in earth surface potentials external to the fence. To avoid the danger of increased voltage exposure from a broken line conductor, suitable guards would be needed to prevent a falling energized line conductor from making physical contact with the fence. Although "inviting," this approach is not practical due to the unknowns of soil strata that make the contours impossible to predict.

The present trend seems to favor a solid bond between the boundary fence and the station ground mat, Appropriate potential grading shields are buried below grade adjacent to the fence on the outside of the substation area to control the step and touch potential exposure to acceptable values (see References [2], [4], [7], and [22]).

It is very important to avoid a metallic extension from the station structure to some point outside the fenced area, which is exposed to contact by persons or animals. Such an extension might take the form of a water pipe, an air pipe, a messenger cable, etc, seemingly having no electrical function. What it does do is convey the potential of the station ground mat to the far end of the metal extension. The earth surface potential drops off fairly rapidly as one moves away from the boundary fence. The 50% voltage contour will be reached in a short distance away from a small station and in a longer separation distance from a large station. Even a fairly large station will display a 50% dropoff in surface potential within 10 ft (3 m). Thus, it would be entirely possible for a person standing on earth and touching a pipe extension from the station structure only 10 ft (3 m) removed from the enclosing fence to be subject to an electric shock voltage of 50% of the ground mat voltage of the station. A station ground mat voltage of 5000 V is not at all unusual for stations operating in the 4.16 to 33 kV range.

2.5 Outdoor Unit Substations

While the functional objectives remain unchanged, the concentration of apparatus items into a single metal-enclosed package (see Fig 39) greatly simplifies the equipment-grounding system plan. Even the presence of a single separate line terminating structure adds little complexity.

Figure 39—Outdoor Unit Substation

The grounding conductor associated with each electric circuit to and from the substation is continued to the substation proper and terminated on the grounding bus provided there. This conductor should be of the prescribed cross section for the capacity of circuit involved and should be run with as close physical spacing to the power conductors as is feasible.

The problem of avoiding dangerous electric-shock-voltage exposure to persons in proximity to the enclosing fence involves the same considerations as in the case of open frame substations. Within the confines of many industrial plants, impedance grounding (either low or high) is used to limit the level of ground-fault current (400 A being a common value for low impedance grounding). This reduces the voltage gradients around the substation so that no fenced enclosure is needed. Persons can be permitted to approach and touch the substation enclosure without risk of dangerous electric-shock exposure. Of course, the grounding bus and enclosure frame of the substation must be connected to the building grounding system, whether or not a local grounding electrode system is installed.

If the substation structure is exposed to lighting or contains surge arresters, the installation should include an appropriate grounding electrode. The reinforcing bars contained on the below-grade foundation structure will usually provide this function adequately (see Reference [18]).

2.6 Installations Serving Heavy Portable Electric Machinery

Introduced in 1.11 in regard to system supply, this area usually involves such equipment as power shovels, draglines, and many mine installations, and it represents one of the more difficult problems in avoiding dangerous electric shock voltage exposure. The mobility of the utilization equipment, and frequently of portable power equipment, precludes installation of a localized ground mat, such as would be employed at a fixed location. A safety ground system is utilized to ensure adequate grounding and personnel safety, and both ac and dc equipment can be employed. This section describes various techniques of grounding such utilization equipment. The illustrations used in this section have excluded overload and short circuit protection schemes to emphasize the grounding system. Except where noted below, all relaying acts to trip an associated circuit interrupter and remove power from the affected equipment. Figure 27 (1.11) illustrates an all ac distribution and utilization system. Figure 40(a) shows only the utilization system portion involving equipment grounding. This portable switchgear application indicates the utilization equipment is operating at the distribution voltage, and examples of this arrangement include heavy portable electric machinery, such as found in surface mining. Ground-fault current limits and relaying pickups are as stated in 1.11. For utilization voltages greater than 1000 V, the objective is to limit the maximum equipment frame potential to 100 V or less during ground fault conditions by selecting the grounding resistor in the substation. Figure 40(b) relates to applications where a portable power center (or unit substation) is connected to distribution (or primary distribution), implying that utilization equipment is operating at a lower voltage than distribution. The power transformer configuration is selected to separate ground fault conditions in the utilization portion from distribution (i.e., delta-wye, delta-delta, or wye-delta connected). The pickup for all ground-fault relays is typically set at 40% of the established ground-current limit. Zero sequence relaying (50G) provides primary protection (residual relaying is sometimes used), and potential relaying (59) about the grounding resistor can be used for backup ground fault protection. The backup relays are often definite time with typical delays from 0.1 to 0.25 s.

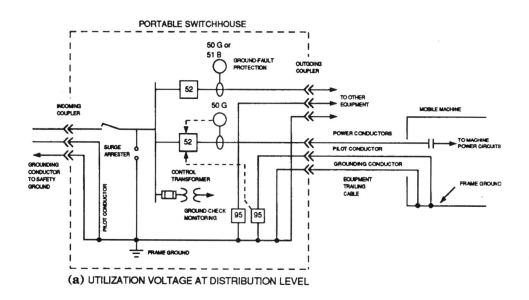

(a) UTILIZATION VOLTAGE AT DISTRIBUTION LEVEL

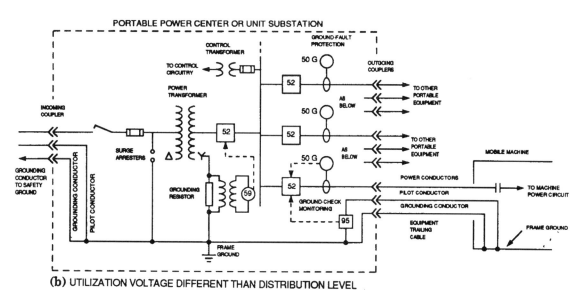

(b) UTILIZATION VOLTAGE DIFFERENT THAN DISTRIBUTION LEVEL

Figure 40—Frame Grounding of AC Portable or Mobile Machinery as Part of a Safety Ground System

Ground current limits vary as to application and system voltage. For utilization equipment at less than 1000 V, the maximum ground current limit must be 25 A or less, but common practice is 15 A. The 100 V maximum frame potential limit (for sizing the grounding resistor) applies to surface or underground utilization equipment greater than 1000 V. This frame potential includes that which might be developed across the grounding conductors (in the distribution system) to the safety ground bed. Regardless, a ground current limit from 15 to 25 A is typical.

An exception to the above ground current limits is found in underground gassy mines (e.g., coal) for face-mining equipment. Recent trends in longwall mining have been toward 2400 or 4160 V utilization. Here, the maximum ground-fault current must be limited to 6.5 or 3.75 A, respectively. Maximum ground-fault relay pickup is again 40% of the current limit, and potential relaying about the grounding resistor for backup protection is required. In the direction of improving personnel safety, some U.S. mines with 2400 V face equipment (individual equipment powers are up to 1100 hp) are using 625 mA ground current limits and are successfully employing a ground fault relaying pickup at 90 mA for primary protection.

Ground-check monitoring to verify grounding conductor continuity is required on all ac portable or mobile (heavy) utilization equipment. Use of an insulated pilot conductor is shown in Fig 40; however, pilotless-type monitors find wide application. Ground-check monitoring is not required on utilization equipment used for long-term fixed location installations.

In many mine power systems, particularly underground, some ac distribution power is converted to dc to power trolley systems and mobile dc equipment. The mobile machinery is typically powered from rectifiers located in the mining area, oftentimes included in a power center also serving ac utilization equipment. Except for the trolley system, all dc utilization equipment is also connected (along with the ac equipment) via grounding conductors to a common safety ground bed.

Figure 41 shows three equipment-grounding schemes with varying ground fault protection. The first two are preferred on a safety standpoint and utilize a separate grounding conductor. Figure 41(a) illustrates neutral shift relaying, employing detection by two dc unbalance relays (64). While sensitive, this scheme is not selective for multiple dc equipment loads. Figure 41(b) shows the use of differential current dc ground fault protection, where a grounding resistor limits dc ground-fault current, typically to 15 A. Ground faults are detected using either a saturable reactor or saturable transformer relaying scheme. Both techniques only sense dc unbalance in the conductors that pass through the sensor; thus, selective dc ground fault relaying can be realized. Typical relay pickup is from 4 to 6 A.

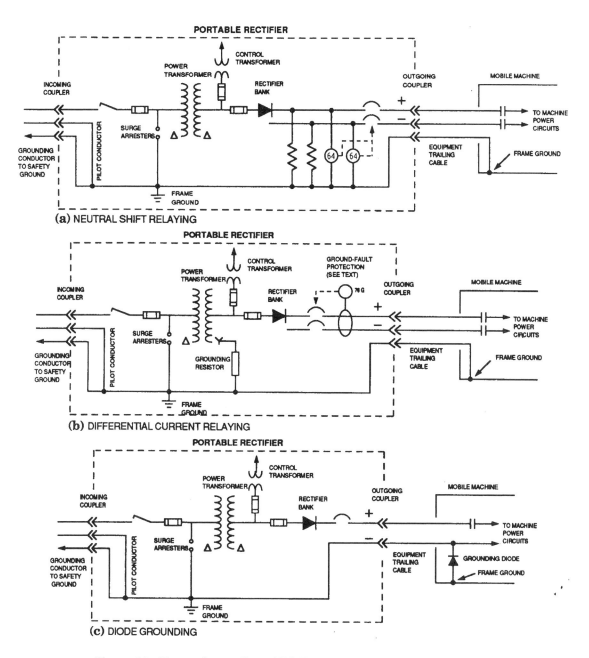

Figure 41—Frame Grounding of DC Portable or Mobile Machinery as Part of a Safety Ground System

The diode ground system in Fig 41(c) permits the use of a two conductor cable without a separate grounding conductor. The machine frame is tied to the grounded negative conductor by means of a grounding diode. In series with the diode is a ground-fault device (not shown on the Figure) having a pickup setting no greater than 25% of the forward-current rating of the diode. The device trips the contactors located in the machine. Major disadvantages of this scheme are (1) some ground faults cannot be detected, (2) only faults downstream from the machine contactors can be cleared, and (3) the diode can fail in an open mode, ungrounding the frame.

As shown in Fig 42, neither conductor to a dc trolley system (rail haulage) is tied to the rectifier station frame ground. However, because the track contacts the mine floor (earth), the negative conductor for the trolley system is grounded, often with a low resistance. For this reason, the ac grounding system must be isolated from the trolley system; otherwise, dc may appear in the ac grounding system. If an ac ground current is present, it will be offset by the dc level. Two undesirable effects of dc offset currents on the ac grounding system are nuisance tripping and intermachine arcing. To help minimize problems, either the rectifier stations should not be located closer than 25 ft (7.6 m) from the track or the rectifier frames should be insulated from the floor.

2.7 Interior Wiring Systems

2.7.1 General

In about the year 1893, a nationwide code of acceptable installation practice for electric power systems within buildings, such as residences, factories, and commercial buildings, was adopted. These rules are now a publication of the NFPA and are documented in the NEC (Reference [1]. This document is reviewed every three years on the basis of suggestions or criticisms submitted by interested individuals or organizations, and revisions or amendments are made accordingly. Article 250 of the NEC (Reference [1]) is devoted to the subject of grounding. All equipment-grounding system designs for installation within buildings of the types named should recognize and conform to the minimum requirements contained in the NEC. Basically, the NEC designates minimum acceptable limits for safety that may not be adequate for a particular application and may not necessarily provide for the efficient or practical use of high technology utilization equipment. The minimum requirements should be expanded in a more conservative direction as far as the system designer considers appropriate based on specific project and site conditions and in accordance with the recommendations of this *Recommended Practice*.

2.7.2 Service Equipment

The term "service equipment" (see the NEC, Reference [1], Article 230) applies to the switching and protective equipment installed where the electric power from the utility is considered to enter the building or site. The required installation practices and protective equipment employed at and downstream of the service equipment are designed to ensure an electric power system that will not create fire or explosion hazards, dangerous electric-shock-voltage exposure to occupants, or an unfavorable electrical ambient condition within buildings. The electric power conductors from the utility that delivers power to the establishment, the service entrance conductors, do not enjoy the quality of protection afforded all circuits extending beyond the service equipment. An electric fault in these conductors may create a severe arcing fault that may persist for an extended interval and represent a dangerous source of fire ignition. The NEC rules make clear the intent that all grounding electrodes, including water piping and metal building frames, be bonded to the equipment-grounding system at the service equipment.

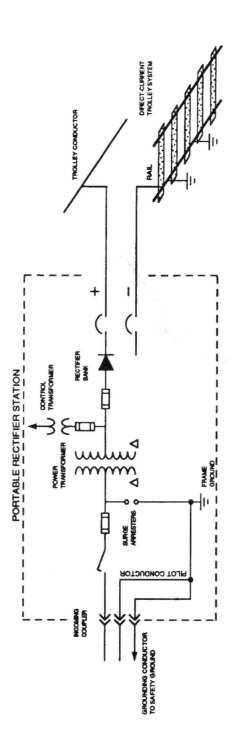

Figure 42—Grounding Connections of DC Trolley Systems Fed by a Safety Ground System

The intended overall purpose of the grounding rules is to achieve, as nearly as practical, a zero potential difference condition between electrical equipment-grounding conductors, the frames of electrical equipment, metal raceways that enclose electrical conductors, and the various items of exposed metal building frames and metal piping within the building. To any person within the building, this absence of electric-shock voltage exposure continues unchanged, even though the grounded electric service conductor assumes a substantial voltage deviation from mean earth potential.

The creation of voltage differences between these designated exposed metal parts within the building will be the result of unplanned, unwanted current flow through these conducting members, usually as a result of an insulation failure on an energized power conductor.

2.7.3 Interior Electric Circuits

With every electric power circuit extending from the service equipment into the building interior that supplies electric power to equipment or apparatus that must be grounded, an equipment-grounding conductor must be run with the power conductors. In most cases the metal conductor enclosure (e.g., tubular metal raceway or cable armor) or cable tray itself is permitted to serve as the grounding conductor (see Reference [1], Article 250-91[b]). The equipment and apparatus requirement for grounding is accomplished by an electrical bond between the frame (or structure) of such equipment (or apparatus) and the equipment-grounding conductor run with that electric circuit. The grounding conductor is not intended to carry nor should it be connected to carry any normal-load current. Thus, the grounding conductor maintains the desired zero potential difference concept throughout the extent of the equipment-grounding conductor harness. Only when unplanned, unwanted fault currents flow along these conductors will there be observed voltage differences.

2.7.4 Thermal Withstand

2.7.4.1 General

When metallic conduit is used as an equipment-grounding conductor, no special considerations are necessary for fault duty of the conduit. When a copper conductor is used to supplement the metallic conduit or where a conductor is necessary, such as in nonmetallic conduit, the design should be evaluated to ensure that the conductor thermal rating is not exceeded. Exceeding the thermal rating can have two effects:

1) Increased temperature can damage the insulation either of the equipment-grounding conductor in case it is insulated or of adjacent phase conductors, especially when the grounding conductor is bare, rendering them unusable following fault clearing.
2) Excessive temperature can fuse the equipment-grounding conductor, clearing the fault current path but rendering faulted equipment unsafe due to elevated voltages.

Thermal stress is expressed in terms of I^2t where I is the rms fault current and t is the time to clear the fault. Thermal stress can be excessive due to high current or to long clearing time.

2.7.4.2 Insulation Damage

Damage to thermoplastic, crosslinked polyethylene, and ethylene propylene rubber insulation is defined by the equation:

$$\frac{I^2t}{A} = 0.0297 \log \frac{T_m + 234}{T_i + 234} \tag{4}$$

where

I = fault current through conductor-amperes
A = conductor cross-sectional area-circular mils
t = time of fault-seconds

T_i = initial operating temperature— degrees Celsius
T_m = maximum temperature for no damage—degrees Celsius

The initial temperature, T_i, is often taken as the conductor maximum operating temperature rating rather than the actual operating temperature. This is a conservative approach but may result in conductor oversizing by one trade size.

The maximum temperature, T_m, is given as 150 °C for thermoplastic insulation and 250 °C for cross linked polyethylene and ethylene propylene rubber insulation. If the equipment-grounding conductor is undersized for the fault current and the clearing time, insulation damage to phase conductors in a conduit may occur due to the proximity of the equipment-grounding conductor to the phase conductor. If fusing is a criterion, then a final temperature of 800 °C for copper may be used (see Reference [13]).

2.7.4.3 Automatic Interrupting Devices

All automatic interrupting devices, whether fuse or circuit breaker, require a definite time to accomplish current interruption. Most devices are inverse time in that the clearing time is less if the current is higher. Each device, though, has an upper limit of maximum speed of clearing determined by physical considerations of mass and energy.

Single pole interrupters are used extensively to protect polyphase circuits. A ground fault on one phase could result in an I^2t duty on the equipment-grounding conductor that exceeds its thermal rating, even if the phase interrupter interrupts the faulted phase current with an I^2t let-through no greater than the equipment-grounding conductor rating. Clearing of the faulted phase does not necessarily stop the ground-fault current. Current may flew in the unfaulted phases, through the load, and back to the faulted phase conductor. Since the ground-fault current is reduced due to the longer fault current path through the load, the time for the single pole phase interrupters to operate would be increased. Although the ground-fault current would probably be reduced, the increased time could cause thermal damage.

Three-phase circuit breakers often have adjustable time-current characteristics. In the simplest form, the phase current sensing magnetic or solid state pickup for instantaneous operation may be adjusted from about 300–500% of overcurrent rating at the low end to about 800–1000% of overcurrent rating at the high end. If the ground fault circuit is designed for a minimum of 500% of overcurrent rating, then a high pickup could result in a long response time. There is a tendency to set the instantaneous pickup, whether magnetic or solid state, as high as possible to avoid nuisance tripping due to high initial inrush currents. More sophisticated circuit-breaker trip devices may have adjustable time delays that permit shaping the time-current curve to coordinate with both upstream and downstream devices. There is a tendency to) set the time delay as long as possible to achieve coordination with as many downstream overcurrent protective devices as possible. Setting of high-current pickup to excessively high values or increasing time delays to high values could cause thermal damage in the equipment-grounding conductor.

2.7.4.4 Equipment-Grounding Conductor Sizing

Selection of an equipment-grounding conductor sized in accordance with the NEC, Reference [1], Table 250-95, will not necessarily provide either a "safe" system or one that is free from potential insulation damage. Where a separate equipment-grounding conductor is used to supplement a metallic conduit grounding system, it is difficult to determine the division of fault current between the conductor and the conduit. It is possible that past ground faults in metallic conduit systems have not caused thermal damage because the maximum ground-fault current did not flow through the conductor.

The above considerations do not hold for equipment-grounding conductors in nonmetallic conduit. In this case, all the ground-fault current will flow in the equipment-grounding conductor and thermal damage must be considered. As an example, consider a 400 A feeder with a No. 3 AWG equipment-grounding conductor sized from the reference Table 250-95. Using an initial temperature of 60 °C and a final temperature of 250 °C for cross-linked polyethylene insulation, $I^2t = 17.8 \times 10^6$. If the ground-fault current is designed to be a minimum of 500% of rated current, then the protective device must clear the fault within 4.5 s in order to limit the final temperature to less than 250 °C. Design of the ground-fault current to be a minimum of 800% of rated current will reduce the protective device required clearing time to 1.7 s.

At 500% of rated current, many overcurrent protective devices, both fuse and circuit breaker, will not clear for 5 to 15 s. Thus, it is important that the specific overcurrent device be a part of the equipment-grounding conductor circuit design. Design of the ground-fault current to be a minimum of 800% of rated current or increasing the size of the equipment-grounding conductor will permit standard overcurrent devices to adequately protect equipment-grounding conductors from the thermal damage. Alternatively, faster acting overcurrent devices or ground fault sensing equipment may be used.

2.7.4.5 Ground Fault Sensing

Use of a phase overcurrent device to detect and clear a ground fault is not ideal. The phase overcurrent device may be designed to withstand overloads for a considerable length of time and yet be able to clear very high fault currents. Ground faults are typically low level and may be less than the rating of the phase overcurrent device. Additionally, since ground faults are often of an arcing nature, any delay in clearing the ground fault will result in material damage.

A ground fault can be detected in one of three ways: (1) ground return, (2) zero sequence, and (3) differential current. The three methods are shown in Fig 43.

Ground return sensing is only applicable at the source transformer or generator. (See 1.6.3 for limitations due to multiple sources.) The connection from the transformer to ground is sensed for current flow. Since normal-load current should not return to the source through the ground on this conductor, any current sensed will be a ground-fault current [see Fig 43(a)].

Where the source grounding conductor is not available such as at a feeder location, a single current transformer placed around the phase conductors and the neutral, if it exists, will sense zero sequence or ground currents. [See Fig 43(b).] If no ground-fault current exists, the magnetic fields of each of the load conductors will cancel and there will be no output from the current transformer. If a ground-fault current exists, then there is a net zero sequence current in the load conductors, and the resultant magnetic field is sensed by the current transformer.

Where current transformers are necessary for phase overcurrent protection, detection of ground-fault current can be obtained by a summation of the phase currents. If a ground-fault current exists, then the net sum of the phase currents and the neutral, if it exists, will not be zero. The connection shown in Fig 43(c) provides a vector sum of the load current. If the sum is not zero, the differential current will flow in the ground-fault relay. The ground fault relay can be made extremely sensitive to low level ground faults and can operate with minimal delay. Its output is used to open an interrupting device and clear the ground fault.

2.8 Interior Unit Substations and Switching Centers

2.8.1 Switching Centers

Switching centers of modern vintage will for the most part consist of integral factory-designed metal-enclosed equipment. All internal components will be prepositioned to meet the applicable industry standards. Within this structure the requirements for grounding conductors will have been recognized and supposedly provided for. With the knowledge that ground-fault current will seek a path in close physical proximity to the phase conductor that carries this current in the outgoing direction (see References [5], [15], [16], and [21]) it is appropriate to make a casual inspection to confirm that these requirements have been properly recognized.

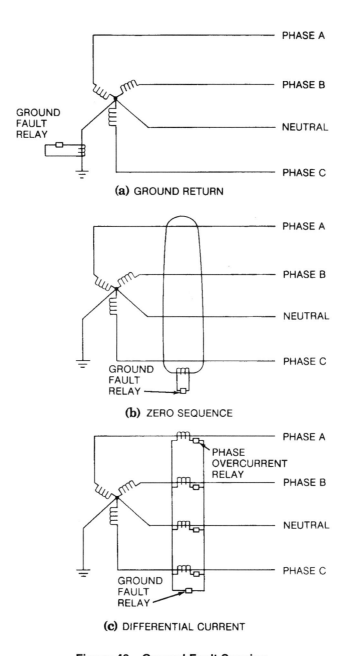

Figure 43—Ground Fault Sensing

The field installation problem boils down to a very simple one of assuring the integrity of the equipment-grounding conductors. Attention should be given to the proper termination of the equipment-grounding conductor associated with each circuit entering the equipment. The equipment-grounding conductor shall meet the cross-section requirements of that circuit. The physical routing should meet the objectives previously named. The terminating fittings should meet the requirements of an electrical junction expected to safely accommodate the high-magnitude short-time current flow. The terminating point on the switching structure should reflect the same capability.

One of the most neglected spots is the termination of a metal raceway when it is used as the equipment-grounding conductor. Commonly, the switching structure contains no metal floor plate. The raceways, typically metal conduits, have been stubbed up through a concrete floor so as to terminate within the open floor area inside the boundaries set by the vertical side sheets of the equipment. The following two grounding conductor errors appear quite often:

1) The metal raceways or cable trays are not recognized as an electrical conductor (the equipment-grounding conductor), and no connection is made to the stub end extending into the equipment enclosure.
2) The grounding lead from the raceway is thought to be needed only as a static drain and is connected to the ground bus with only a No. 12 AWG (3.3 mm(2)) conductor.

Metal raceways that serve as the equipment-grounding conductor and terminate at the side sheets or cover plate of the equipment enclosure should be made up tight with double locknuts and supplemented with a bonding jumper. Proper termination of the raceway system to the equipment enclosure can prevent burnouts at the connection of sheet metal panels to each other with bolts or sheet metal screws, serious damage to the equipment, and injury to personnel.

2.8.2 Transformation Unit Substations

Transformation unit substations (see Figs 44 and 45) present some additional problems. The electrical system derived from the transformer secondary represents a new electrical system with its own equipment-grounding system requirements.

The treatment of all primary circuits entering the structural housing should be designed with the same criteria used for a simple switching structure. An effective grounding conductor running back to the source of primary power is required in case of a circuit fault to ground at any point along the primary circuits, within the enclosure containing the stepdown transformer, within the primary circuit switching device, or within the transformer itself.

Figure 44—Indoor Unit Substation — Typical Unitized Assembly

**Figure 45—Indoor Unit Substation — Back View Showing Use of an
Independent Grounding Conductor with Each Circuit**

The secondary winding of the step-down transformer constitutes the point of origin of a new electrical system. It will be to this point that ground-fault currents associated with the radiating secondary circuits return. Hence, all secondary circuit equipment-grounding conductors are brought to a common junction point at this source transformer. For grounded system operation, this common junction point is bonded to the grounded circuit conductor (on the supply side of any overcurrent device or disconnecting means), to the source transformer frame or other metal enclosures, and to any adjacent metal member of the building structure or piping system if available. Should the secondary system be exposed to external sources of overvoltage surges, such as lightning, a check should be made to ensure the existence of an adequate grounding electrode connected to the central junction of secondary grounding conductors.

In general, the grounding electrode will be present for system grounding; however, the requirements for system grounding may not be adequate for the dissipation of lightning surges.

In most cases, it will be observed that the primary and secondary grounding conductor systems become interconnected at the step-down substation. This happens by mere coincidence because the metal enclosure at the substation encloses energized conductors of both the primary system and the secondary system. Functionally, the two grounding conductor systems are independent of each other. (Had the transformation station consisted of an independent generator belt driven from an electric drive motor, the independence of the two grounding conductor systems would have been self evident.)

2.9 Utilization Equipment

The equipment-grounding function at utilization equipment consists simply of providing an effective bonding connection between the nonelectrical metal parts of the terminal apparatus, which either enclose or are adjacent to energized conductors, and the equipment-grounding conductor. The sizing and terminating of all such grounding conductors shall observe the same rules already established, which depend on the rating and character of the next upstream overcurrent protective device. In many cases where the electrical metal raceway or cable armor serves as the equipment-grounding conductor of the circuit, the bonding connection to the utilization equipment frame consists simply of a good mechanical connection where the metal raceway terminates at the connection box or metal side or roof sheet of the terminal apparatus.

A bonding connection to adjacent building metal structure in the case of fixed equipment is appropriate, although somewhat redundant. A separate equipment-grounding conductor wire provides added assurance of continuity of the equipment ground.

Figure 46 displays the desired equipment to grounding conductor connection arrangement for a variety of power circuit patterns and clearly displays the distinction between the "grounding" and the "grounded" conductors.

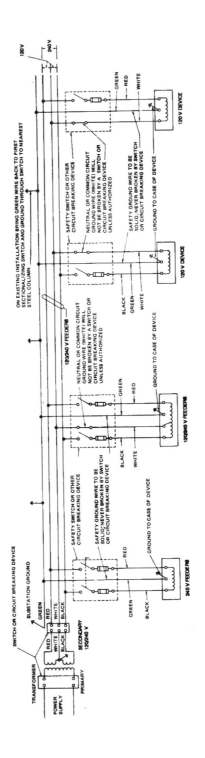

(a) FIXED EQUIPMENT

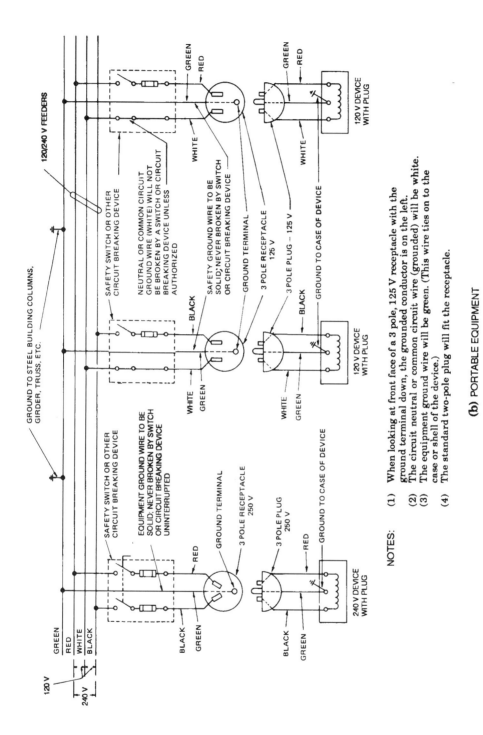

Figure 46—Typical Supply-Conductor Patterns of Power Circuits of Utilization Apparatus with Emphasis on a Distinction Between Grounding and Grounded Conductors

2.10 References

[1] ANSI/NFPA 70-1990, National Electrical Code.[8]

[2] IEEE Std 80-1986, Guide for Safety in AC Substation Grounding (ANSI).[9]

[3] IEEE Std 141-1986, Recommended Practice for Electric Power Distribution for Industrial Plants (IEEE Red Book) (ANSI).

[4] Armstrong, H. R., and Simpkin, L. T. "Grounding Electrode Potential Gradients from Model Tests," *AIEE Transactions on Power Apparatus and Systems*, vol. 79, Oct 1960, pp. 618-623.

[5] Beeman, D. L., Ed. *Industrial Power Systems Handbook*. New York: McGraw-Hill, 1955.

[6] Bisson, A. J., and Rochau, E. A. "Iron Conduit Impedance Effects in Ground Circuit Systems," *AIEE Transactions on Applications and Industry*, vol. 73, July 1954, pp. 104–107.

[7] Bodle, D. W. "Earth Potential Distribution Associated with Power Grounding Structures," AIEE Conference Paper CP 62-205, 1962.

[8] Coleman, W. E., and Frostick, H. G. "Electrical Grounding and Cathodic Protection at the Fairless Works," *AIEE Transactions on Applications and Industry*, vol. 74, Mar 1955, pp. 19–24.

[9] Gienger, J. A., Davidson, O. C., and Brendell, R. W. "Determination of Ground-Fault Current on Common AC Grounded-Neutral Systems in Standard Steel or Aluminum Conduit," *AIEE Transactions on Applications and Industry*, vol. 79, May 1960, pp. 84–90.

[10] Gienger, J. A., and Lloyd, R. L. *Bibliography on Electrical Safety/1930 through 1953*, Sec. C, AIEE Publication S-69, 1969.[10]

[11] Goers, R. E. "Quiet-Wiring Zone," Conference Record of the 1968 Third Annual Meeting of the IEEE Industry and General Applications Group, pp. 249–253.

[12] "Grounding," in *McGraw-Hill Encyclopedia of Science and Technology*, New York: McGraw-Hill, 1970.

[13] Kaufmann, R. H. "Application Limitations of Single-Pole Interrupters in Poly-Phase Industrial and Commercial Building Power Systems," *IEEE Transactions (Applications and Industry)*, vol. 82, Nov. 1963, pp. 363–368.

[14] Kaufman, R. H. "Important Functions Performed by an Effective Equipment Grounding System," *IEEE Transactions on Industry and General Applications*, vol. IGA-6, No.6, Nov./Dec. 1970, pp. 545–552.

[15] Kaufmann, R. H. "Let's Be More Specific About Equipment Grounding," *American Power Conference Transactions*, 1962; General Electric Bulletin GER-1974.

[16] Kaufmann, R. H. "Some Fundamentals of Equipment-Grounding Circuit Design," *AIEE Transactions on Applications and Industry*, vol. 73, Nov. 1954, pp. 227–232.

[17] Kaufman, R. H. "The Magic of I^2t," *IEEE Transactions on Industry and General Applications*, vol. IGA-2, Sept/Oct 1966, pp. 384–392.

---

[8]NFPA publications are available from Publications Sales, National Fire Protection Association, 1 Batterymarch Park, P.O. Box 9101, Quincy, MA 02269-9101, USA.
[9]IEEE publications are available from the Institute of Electrical and Electronics Engineers, 445 Hoes Lane, P.O. Box 1331, Piscataway, NJ 08855-1331, USA.
[10]This publication is out of print. It is in the collection of the Engineering Societies Library, 345 East 47th Street, New York, NY 10017.

[18] Lee, R.H., and Fagan, E. J. "The Use of Concrete-Enclosed Reinforcing Rods as Grounding Electrodes," *Conference Record of the 1969 Fourth Annual Meeting of the IEEE Industry and General Applications Group*, pp. 155–166.

[19] Redding, D., and O'Brien, A. "Large Loss Fires in the United States during 1984," *Fire Journal*, Nov. 1985, pp. 17–25, 68–84.

[20] Schmidt, W. C. "Electrical Noise in Control System Installations," *Conference Record of the 1968 Third Annual Meeting of the IEEE Industry and General Applications Group*, pp. 229–238.

[21] Soares, E. C. "Grounding Electrical Distribution Systems for Safety," Wayne, NJ: March Publishing Company, 1966.

[22] Thapar, B., and Purl, K. K. "Mesh Potentials in High-Voltage Grounding Grids," *IEEE Transactions on Power Apparatus and Systems*, vol. PAS-86, Feb. 1967, pp. 249–254.

[23] Willard, G. "The Prevention and Treatment of Noise in Control Signals," *Conference Record of the 1968 Third Annual Meeting of the IEEE Industry and General Applications Group*, pp. 239–248.

2.11 Bibliography

Bullard, "W. R. Grounding Principles and Practice IV: System Grounding," *Electrical Engineering*, vol. 64, Apr. 1945, pp. 145–151.

Code for Protection Against Lightning (Handbook 46). Boulder, CO: U.S. Department of Commerce, National Bureau of Standards.

Dalziel, C. F. "Dangerous Electric Currents," *AIEE Transactions*, vol. 65, 1946, pp. 579–584 and 1123–1124.

Dalziel, C. F. "Effects of Electric Shock on Man," *IRE Transactions on Medical Electronics*, vol. PGME-5, July 1956, pp. 44–62.

Elek, A. "Proper Grounding Reduces Hazards," *Electrical World*, Feb 16, 1959, p. 78.

Horn, R. S. "Ground Your Power Station Safely," *Power Engineering*, Jan 1959, p. 85.

Jensen, C. "Grounding Principles and Practice-II: Establishing Grounds." *Electrical Engineering*, vol. 64, Feb. 1945, pp. 68–74.

Johnson, A. A. "Grounding Principles and Practice-III: Generator-Neutral Grounding Devices," *Electrical Engineering*, vol. 64, Mar 1945, pp. 92–99.

Kaufman, R. H., and Page, J. C. "Arcing Fault Protection for Low-Voltage Power Distribution Systems—Nature of the Problem," *AIEE Transactions on Power Apparatus and Systems*, vol. 79, June 1960, pp. 160–167.

Lee, R. H. "Ground Fault Magnitude Determination and Human Safety from Fault-Return Path Impedance," *Conference Record of the 1967 Second Annual Meeting of the IEEE Industry and General Applications Group*, pp. 487–498.

Lee, R. H. "Impedance of Trays as Fault Return Conductors," *Conference Record of the 1967 Second Annual Meeting of the IEEE Industry and General Applications Group*, pp. 477–485.

Mackenzie, W. F. "Impedance and Induced Voltage Measurements on Iron Conductors," *AIEE Transactions on Communication and Electronics*, vol. 73, June 1954, pp. 577–581.

O'Conner, J. J. "Industrial Electrical Systems Reliability Takes on Added Meaning," *IEEE Transactions on Industry and General Applications*, vol. IGA-4, July/Aug. 1968, pp. 354–355.

Peach, N. "Protect Low-Voltage Systems from Arcing Fault Damage," *Power Magazine*, Apr 1964.

Power Distribution Systems of Open Pit Mines. General Electric Company, Technical Bulletin GET 238 1A.

Rudenberg, R. "Grounding Principles and Practice I: Fundamental Considerations on Ground Currents," *Electrical Engineering*, vol. 64, Jan 1945, pp. 1–13.

Shields, F. J. "The Problem of Arcing Faults in Low-Voltage Power Distribution Systems,," *IEEE Transactions on Industry and General Applications*, vol. IGA-3, Jan./Feb. 1967, pp. 15–25.

Chapter 3

Static and Lightning Protection Grounding

3.1 Introduction

This chapter covers static electricity, its generation, proven methods of safeguarding from the hazards of this phenomenon by grounding and other methods, and lightning-protection grounding.

A detailed study of static electricity is not made in this section. For more derailed information on this subject, various references are cited (see [20], [21], [26-29], [32], [37], and [38].[11] This material will serve as a guide for electrical engineers who are involved with this phenomenon so that they can recognize a hazardous situation and provide suitable safeguards.

Lightning-protection grounding is essential for the protection of buildings, transmission lines, and electrical equipment from lightning discharges and surges. A brief description is given of the nature of lightning; the need for protection against lightning for various types of structures, buildings, and equipment; the requirements for protection; and of practices for protection and grounding. This section does not cover details of calculations in sizing lightning diverters and methods of selecting lightning protective devices. The engineer responsible for lightning protection is advised to use the referenced materials to make an analytical study of this subject.

3.2 Static Grounding

3.2.1 Purpose of Static Grounding

The accumulation of static electricity on equipment, on materials being handled or processed, and on operating personnel introduces a potentially serious hazard in any occupancy where flammable or explosive liquids, gases, dusts, or fibers are present.

The discharge of an accumulation of static electricity from an object to ground or to another charged object of different voltage can be the cause of a fire or an explosion if it takes place in the presence of readily flammable materials or combustible vapor and air mixtures. Such fires and explosions have caused injury to personnel and loss of life, as well as millions of dollars of loss in property damage and business interruption.

Protection of human life is the first objective in attempting to control static charges. Besides the danger to lives from explosions or fires that may result from a static spark, there is also the danger that a person, becoming startled when suddenly subjected to a static shock, may fall or accidentally come into contact with some moving equipment. The second aim in eliminating or mitigating static electricity is to prevent losses in the following categories:

1)   Capital investment in buildings and equipment due to fires or explosions
2)   Operating costs for storing flammable materials
3)   Overhead and loss of production due to fires or explosions
4)   Capital investment in sensitive electronic equipment due to excessive or rapidly changing voltage
5)   Loss of electronically stored data due to voltage transients

If losses such as those listed can be avoided by proper static control, the expenditure required to secure this protection is good insurance.

An additional need for static control may be for the improvement in manufacturing operations or in product quality. For example, static in grinding operations can prevent grinding to a fine degree. Static in certain textile operations

---

[11]The numbers in brackets correspond to those of the references in 3.4.

causes fibers to stand on end instead of lying fiat, which often affects the quality of the material. Static charges on materials handled by chutes or ducts have been known to cause clogging as a result of materials clinging to the inside of the chutes and ducts. In the printing industry, the control of static electricity is important to prevent damage to the printed images by the attraction of dust particles, and to prevent attraction of the ink to the underside of sheets that may be stacked above them, as well as to avoid possible ignition of vapors from flammable inks and solvents used in the process.

There are many other manufacturing processes or operations where static accumulations are either a fire or an explosion hazard or cause inferior products; for example, in grain elevators; in coating, spreading, and impregnating operations; with conveyor belts and pulleys; dry cleaning; blending and mixing; and filling of tank cars, barges, trucks, aircraft, or other containers with flammable liquids. Each process or operation may require a different method to safeguard against the hazard. This is achieved by providing means whereby charges may recombine harmlessly before sparking or by preventing accumulation of charges by grounding or bonding, humidification, or ionization.

3.2.2 Fundamental Causes of Static Electricity

3.2.2.1 Theory of Static Generation

Static electricity is probably the earliest reported manifestation of electricity. The Greeks are on record as having observed this phenomenon in about 600 BC. They noticed that a piece of amber, when rubbed with another material, had the ability to attract or repel other objects of light weight, but scientific investigation of the phenomenon did not begin until some 23 centuries later.

In a neutral or uncharged body, the electrons, which are the negative components of the atom, and the protons, which are the positive components, are present in exactly equal numbers, and these can be separated only by the expenditure of energy, usually in mechanical, thermal, or chemical form. Electrons are free to move from one molecule to another in solid conductive materials. Protons cannot move appreciably unless the atom moves. Only electrons are mobile in solids, whereas both electrons and protons are free to move in gases and liquids.

Static electricity is generated by the movement of electrons, which occurs when unlike materials are in contact with each other and are then separated. When two unlike materials are in intimate contact, electrons from one material move across the interface to the surface of the other, and their counterparts (protons) in equal numbers remain on the other body; an attractive force is thus established as equilibrium is achieved. When bodies are separated, electrons produce electrical charges on the objects separated, which shows as an increase in voltage between the two surfaces.

If two materials that are good conductors are in contact with each other and are then separated, most of the excess electrons in one will return to the other before the separation is complete. But if either or both of them is an insulator and both are not grounded, both will display a charge because some of the excess electrons will be entrapped in one of them when separation occurs, and the insulating body is said to be *charged*. Actually, static charge is due to an excess or a deficiency in electrons, and a surface that has an excess or deficiency of one electron in every 100 000 atoms is very strongly charged. The voltage developed due to electrical charges is related to the amount of charge deposited on a body and to the capacitance of this body with respect to its surroundings. The relationship is expressed by the following:

$$V = \frac{Q}{C} \tag{5}$$

where

V = voltage, in V
Q = charge, in C
C = capacitance, in F

This voltage can continue to grow on an insulating body under the influence of continuous charge generation. At some voltage, the leakage of charge will be equal to the rate at which the charge is being placed on the insulated body, and a stabilized condition will be reached. If the leakage of charge through the insulating body is not rapid enough, a sparking voltage will be reached, and sparking will occur before stabilization is reached.

The voltage increase on separation could reach several thousand volts, but the charge is relatively immobile, so a spark from an insulated surface will usually not produce ignition.

Static electricity is usually generated by the following:

1) Pulverized materials passing through chutes or pneumatic conveyors
2) Belt drives when belts are of nonconductive material
3) Gas, steam, or air flowing through an opening
4) Motion that involves changes in the relative position of contacting surfaces, usually of unlike materials, liquid or solid, at least one of which usually is a poor conductor of electricity
5) The human body in a low-humidity area may accumulate a dangerous static charge of several thousand volts by contact of shoes with floor coverings or by working close to machinery that generates static electricity

3.2.2.2 Conditions Affecting the Production of Static Charges

The possibility of producing electrification (static charge) and the degree that it will be produced will depend mainly on the following:

1) Material characteristics
2) Speed of separation
3) Area in contact
4) Effect of motion between substances
5) Atmospheric conditions

These conditions are defined as follows:

Material Characteristics. It has been previously stated that one of the materials or substances must have higher insulating properties than the other to at least some degree to generate a static charge between them. The physical forms may be solids, liquids, or gases. The solids may be in the form of sheeting, rods, etc., or may be broken up into particles that form a dust. The degree of electrostatic charge that may exist between two materials will be proportional to the difference in their dielectric constants. Even metals have dielectric constants, that of iron being 4.2, that of copper being 2.1, and that of aluminum being 4.8. For comparison, the dielectric constant of air is approximately 1.0, that of porcelain 5.7–6.8, and that of nylon 3.7–4.1. Also, the positive charge will usually show up on the material having the higher dielectric constant.

Speed of Separation. As the speed of separation of two substances is increased, the chance for impounding the charges on the materials also increases, thus increasing the voltage differences between them. For example, electrification caused by the separation of a moving belt from a pulley increases directly with the belt speed, and electrification of aircraft in flight, caused by atmospheric water particles, dry snow, and ice crystals or dust increases about as the cube of the speed of the aircraft.

Area in Contact. The area of the substances in contact has a direct bearing on the degree of electrification because a larger contact area means that more charge may be transferred from one substance to the other, though the charge density may be the same. In other words, the larger body receives or accumulates the larger quantity of charge.

Effect of Motion Between Substances. Static electricity has often been called frictional electricity, but actually friction plays little part in the process of electrification, although the rubbing together does increase electrification. This is because in the process of rubbing, more peaks on the surfaces are brought into contact, since surfaces that are smooth and flat to the eye are microscopically rough with peaks and valleys, and the electrons travel only where actual contact occurs. Also heating due to friction eases the transfer of electrons. Similarly, liquids sprayed or expelled from a nozzle, particularly if they impinge on a surface, often produce high voltage on the droplets of liquid and on the surface on which they impinge.

Liquid materials in a tank may accumulate static charges (1) as a result of deliberate agitation of the liquid, (2) because of tank motion, or (3) while the tank is being filled.

Another example of motion producing alternate contact and separation of materials is the passing of a belt over a pulley, and as previously pointed out, the higher the speed, the more often these alternations occur and the greater the static charge on the belt. The same principle applies to any sheeting passing over rolls, such as in the manufacture and processing of rubber materials, papers, or textiles. Rubber tires [36] rolling over streets and roads produce the same effect, and may account for static charges on automobiles, tank trucks, etc.

Atmospheric Conditions. The fact that low humidity is related to the production of static is probably well known to everyone because of the personal discomfort experienced in touching a metal object on a dry day after having accumulated a charge by walking across a rug or coming into contact with some other insulating material. This shows clearly the hazard that can exist in an operation that may require controlled low-humidity conditions.

3.2.3 Magnitudes

3.2.3.1 General

The magnitude of static electricity quantities is different from that of power electricity. The voltage difference may reach thousands of volts, currents may be less than a millionth of an ampere ($1 \cdot 10^{-6}$ A), and resistances of less than one million ohms (1 MΩ) may cause a short circuit, as far as electrostatics is concerned.

3.2.3.2 Voltages Possible

Voltages that have been observed in a few industries or have been created in tests are shown in Table 6. From Table 7, it can be seen that even voltages of 30 000 V may jump over 1 in (25.4 mm). Such a spark could readily release enough energy to ignite flammable mixtures.

3.2.4 Conditions Required for a Static Charge to Cause Ignition

In order for a static spark to produce ignition in a combustible vapor and air mixture, there must be sufficient energy stored in the charged body. The amount of energy that is stored and available from a capacitive-type discharge can be calculated by the formula

$$E = \frac{1}{2}(CV^2 \cdot 10^{-9}) \tag{6}$$

where

C = capacitance, in pF
V = voltage, in V
E = energy, in mJ

Table 6—Range of Static Voltages Produced by Various Processes

Type of Equipment	Voltage Range Observed (kV)
Belted drives	60–100
Fabric handling	15–80
Paper machines	5–100
Tank trucks	up to 25
Belt conveyors (grain)	up to 45

Table 7—DC Breakdown Voltages Point to Plane

Distance		Voltage (kV)	
(in)	(mm)	Point +	Plane +
0.197	5	6	11
0.394	10	16	18
0.591	15	20	29
0.787	20	25	39
1.181	30	36	57
1.575	40	42	71
1.969	50	50	85
2.362	60	54	98
2.756	70	60	112
3.150	80	63	124
3.543	90	67	140

The energy necessary for ignition is dependent on several variables, such as the shape and spacing of the electrodes between which the spark occurs and the composition of the gas mixture, the gas temperature, and the pressure. Tests have shown that 0.25 mJ of stored energy is required to ignite an optimum mixture of saturated hydrocarbon gas and air, but where the voltage differences are less than 1500 V and capacitance is less than 222 pF, the resulting sparks are unlikely to cause ignition of such a mixture because the energy developed is less than 0.25 mJ. Acetylene gas used in industrial plants for cutting metal is exceptionally flammable. It needs only about 0.02 mJ of spark energy to ignite.

Approximate values of capacitance, in picofarads, of some objects are as follows:

- Human being 100–400 pF
- Automobile 500 pF
- Tank truck (2000 gal) 1000 pF
- 12 ft (3.6 m) diameter tank with insulated lining 100 000 pF

For static electricity to be able to cause ignition, in addition to the requirement of sufficient energy in the spark discharge, it must take place in an ignitable mixture. If the mixture is too lean or too rich, ignition will not occur.

For a complete discussion of the explosive limits of various gas and liquid mixtures, as well as the spark energy required to ignite such mixtures, see Reference [22].

3.2.5 Measurement and Detection of Static Electricity

3.2.5.1 General

Static electricity has different magnitudes of electrical quantities from power electricity, so the techniques and instruments used for the measurement and detection of static electricity are different. Instruments and devices used in measurements and detection are described in the following paragraphs.

3.2.5.2 Electrostatic Voltmeter

As static charges are characterized by high voltage and low energy, instruments that have practically no current drain must be used for voltage measurements. The electrostatic voltmeter is such an instrument, and while it may not have high accuracy, it is sufficiently accurate to measure voltage for quantitative electrostatic analysis. Electrostatic voltmeters are available in several ranges from 100 V to 5000 V. These meters operate on the principle of electrostatic attraction between movable and stationary metal vanes. Practically no current is passed to maintain deflection. Portable models are available. These meters are moderately expensive, not too rugged, fairly sensitive, and do not indicate polarity.

3.2.5.3 Neon Lamp Tester

This device is very inexpensive and quite sensitive. It can be carried in one's pocket, so occasional checks for static electricity can conveniently be made. It will light up feebly when one terminal is grounded or held in the hand and the other makes contact with the charged body that carries a charge potential of 100 V or more. Adjustable series-parallel groupings of neon lamps and small capacitors can be arranged to give approximate quantitative information.

3.2.5.4 Solid-State Electrometer

This instrument may be used to detect the presence of static electricity, but it should have very high input impedance so as to limit current drain. Instruments are available with an input impedance of 10^{15} Ω

Electrometers use special field-effect solid-state devices having a very high input resistance and drawing a very low input current. The meter uses batteries, so it must be switched on before entering a charged area and switched off after leaving the area.

3.2.5.5 Electrometer Amplifier

This instrument is generally used for the investigation of static electricity in the field and laboratory. It employs high resistance in the input circuit, and thus has low current drain. It can be used as either a voltmeter, a chargemeter, or a current meter. It is quite sophisticated and expensive and needs experienced operators to use it.

3.2.5.6 Generating Voltmeter

A generating voltmeter, occasionally called a *field mill*, is a device to measure electrical field strength and produces an alternating current proportional to the electrical field by electrostatic induction, much as a conventional alternator produces alternating current by electromagnetic induction. This alternating current is electronically amplified, then rectified, and the output is fed to an indicating meter. The generating voltmeter usually consists either of a motor-driven variable capacitor or of linearly vibrating capacitor plates exposed to the electric field. The capacitor serves to *chop* the electric field, creating a periodically varying charge, which results in ac output. A chief drawback to the practical usefulness of the generating voltmeter, as normally built and used, is interpreting the meaning of its indication in a nonsymmetrical geometric environment.

3.2.5.7 Charge Density Meter

This is a variation of the generating voltmeter, which is designed to operate immersed in a charged insulating liquid. The device is usually used in a pipe or with a constant-geometry outer shield. Under such conditions, the signals from this device can be interpreted in terms of the electrical environment in which it is working. Relaxation of space charges in the charge density meter after flow has been stopped provides a measurement of the liquid conductivity under actual conditions in the system at the location of the meter.

3.2.5.8 Static Electricity Detector

This is a commercially available instrument, which detects the presence of static charges and gives both a visual and an audible alarm. It also contains an indicator to indicate the magnitude of the charge. This device is portable or may be installed in a permanent location with an antenna system installed in the operating areas to pick up the signal if static is present. Such an instrument is listed by Underwriters Laboratories, Inc., for class I, groups A, B, C, and D, and class II, groups E, F, and G hazardous locations. Some instruments may need batteries or line power to operate them. Such instruments must be judiciously handled in hazardous areas to eliminate the possibility of sparks of arcs due to any defect or fault. Test probes used in an area of explosive vapors should be highly insulated to avoid sparks.

3.2.6 Methods of Static Control

3.2.6.1 General

Static electricity generation cannot be prevented, but it can be mitigated or controlled by providing means of recombining separated charges as rapidly as they are produced and before sparking voltages are attained. Methods used are the following:

1) Grounding and bonding
2) Humidity control
3) Ionization
4) Conductive floors
5) Conductive footwear and casters
6) Special precautions
7) Proper maintenance

These methods may also be used in combination for effective control.

3.2.6.2 Grounding and Bonding

Many static problems can be solved by bonding the various parts of the equipment together and grounding the entire system. Bonding (connecting the two objects together) minimizes voltage differences between conductive objects, thus preventing sparking between two bodies, as shown in Figs 47 and 48.

Grounding minimizes voltage differences between objects and the ground, as shown in Fig 49. Bonding and grounding should be done by bare or insulated wire, No. 6 or No. 4 AWG (for mechanical strength), though the current is on the order of microamperes (10^{-6} A). Any ground adequate for power circuits or lightning protection is adequate for protection from static electricity. Even a ground resistance of 1 MΩ is adequate for static grounding. Where grounding or bonding wires are exposed to damage, they should be run in rigid metal conduit or pipe. Equipment or tanks inherently bonded or grounded by their contacts with ground do not need special means of bonding. For moving objects, a grounding brush or wipe of carbon, brass, or spring bronze may be used, as shown in Fig 50.

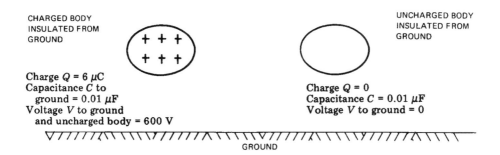

Figure 47—Charged and Uncharged Bodies Insulated from Ground

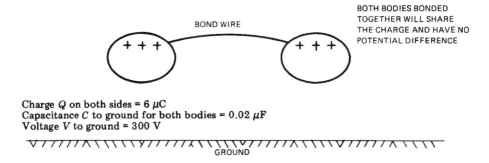

Figure 48—Both Insulated Bodies Share the Same Charge

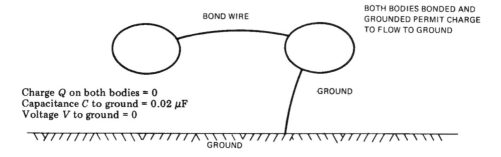

Figure 49—Both Bodies Are Grounded and Have No Charge

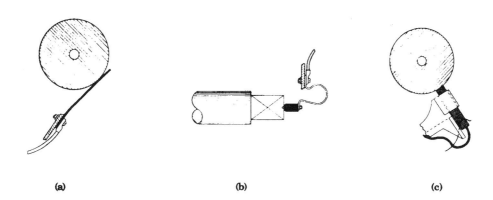

Figure 50—Methods of Grounding Metal Rollers or Shafting: (a) Spring Bronze Brush, (b) Brass or Carbon Brush, (c) Carbon Brush and Holder*
*From Data Sheet 5–8, Static Electricity © 1981 by Factory Mutual Engineering Corporation. Reprinted with permission.

Grounding, however, is not a cure for all static problems. For example, if the material being processed is rather bulky and has high dielectric characteristics, a static charge on the upper portion of the material is usually very effectively insulated from ground, and it may result in a spark discharge. In case of processes involving nonconducting material, such as paper, cloth, or rubber, it is not possible to drain off the static electricity charges by ordinary grounding and bonding. Also, charges may accumulate on the surface of low-conductivity liquids, such as most refined petroleum products. These charges cannot be removed by bonding or grounding. In such cases, other methods of control, such as ionization or humidification, should be utilized.

3.2.6.3 Humidity Control

Many insulating materials, such as fabric, wood, paper, or concrete, contain a certain amount of moisture in equilibrium with the surrounding air. This moisture or relative humidity controls the surface conductivity of these insulating materials. The higher the humidity, the greater the conductivity. For example, the surface conductivity of plate glass at 50% relative humidity is about 1000 times its conductivity at 20% humidity. At normal humidity (30% or more) an invisible film of water provides an electrical leakage path over most solid insulating bodies and the clothes and shoes of a worker, which drains away static charges as fast as they are generated. When relative humidity is 30% or less the same materials dry out and become good insulators, and static manifestations become noticeable and may cause fires from static sparks. Where high humidity does not affect the material adversely, this affords one of the best ways of controlling static electricity. Humidifying the whole atmosphere, or localized humidification, especially near the point where static electricity is accumulating, has proved to be a solution where static electricity has resulted in the adhesion or repulsion of sheets of papers, fibers, etc. In some cases, localized humidification by steam ejection provides satisfactory results without increasing the humidity in the whole area. The minimum value of relative humidity that is required for effective control of static electricity is difficult to determine and will vary with the process and the surrounding conditions. However, it is believed that where the relative humidity is maintained in the range of 60–70% at ordinary indoor temperatures, static accumulations are not likely to reach dangerous proportions. Where the process may be affected adversely by humidity, or where the area may be air conditioned for process control or comfort, and where humidity will not noticeably decrease the resistivity (such as uncontaminated surfaces of most synthetic plastic and the surface of many petroleum liquids), then other methods of static control must be considered.

3.2.6.4 Ionization

In the process of ionization, the air molecules are overstressed; thus electrons are separated from the molecules. The electrons are negatively charged, and the molecules that have lost them become positive in polarity. When a charged object is brought in contact with ionized air, the static charge is dissipated. The charge is either conducted to ground through the ionized air, or the charged object attracts a sufficient number of positively or negatively charged ions from the air to neutralize it. Ionization of air can be obtained by flame, alternating electric fields generated by high voltage ultraviolet light, or radioactivity. This can be achieved by several devices and methods. The most common are static comb or inductive neutralizer, electrical neutralizer, radioactive neutralizer, and open flames.

A static comb or inductive neutralizer is a nonelectrically energized low-cost device. The static comb is a metal bar equipped with a series of sharp needle points or a grounded metal wire surrounded with metallic tinsel (Fig 51). The ionization of air occurs through the charge concentration on the sharp points of the collector from the electric field owing to the charge on the object. The field is concentrated near the pointed object, and when the charge is above a minimum value, spontaneous ionization of air takes place. When a grounded static comb is placed close to the insulated charged body, ionization of the air at the needle points provides enough conductivity to make some of the charge leak away from the object. This method is usually employed to reduce the static charge from fabrics, paper, and power belts.

The electrical neutralizer, now available commercially, produces the conductive ionized air by sharply pointed conductors connected to a high-voltage supply. When placed near the moving or stationary charged surfaces, the charges are thereby neutralized at the surfaces or are leaked away to some adjacent grounded conducting body. These neutralizers are powered by the high-voltage secondary of a small step-up transformer (Fig 52).

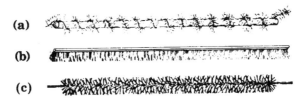

Figure 51—Static Combs (a) Tinsel Spirally Wound on Wooden Bar (b) Crimped Bronze Wire Set in Metal Back (c) Copper or Bronze Bristles Set in Twisted Wire

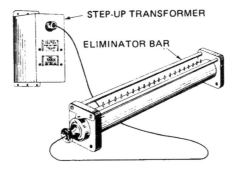

Figure 52—Electrically Energized Neutralizer*
*From Data Sheet 5–8, Static Electricity © 1981 by Factory Mutual Engineering Corporation. Reprinted with permission.

Electrical neutralizers are used for removing static charges from cotton, wool, silk, or paper in process, manufacturing, or printing, but are not recommended in atmospheres having flammable vapors, gases, etc. Necessary precautions must be taken to protect operating and maintenance personnel from high-voltage circuits.

Radioactive neutralizers ionize the air by emission of alpha particles from radioactive material such as radium or polonium. In the application of these neutralizers, care must be taken to avoid harmful effects of radiation. Their use is regulated by the US Nuclear Regulatory Commission.

Ionization of air can also be obtained by rows of small open flames, which may be used in paper printing presses where nonflammable ink is used.

3.2.6.5 Conductive Floors

Where extremely hazardous operating conditions exist, such as in the production of some explosives or in processes involving oxygen-enriched flammable vapor or gas mixtures that are susceptible to static ignition, the use of conductive floors or floor coverings may be required to prevent the accumulation of static charge by grounding personnel and conductive objects together, since the human body in a dry location can also accumulate a dangerous static charge. Where such flooring is required, it should be of nonsparking materials, such as conductive rubber, lead, or other conductive compounds.

The resistance of the floor should be less than 1 000 000 Ω when measured between two electrodes placed 3 ft (0.91 m) apart anywhere on the floor. In addition, to protect personnel against electric-shock hazard, the resistance of the floor should be more than 25 000 Ω when measured between an electrode placed at any point on the floor and a ground connection, and between two electrodes placed 3 ft (0.91 m) apart at any point on the floor. See ANSI/NFPA 99-1990 [13], Section 12-4.1.3.8(b) (7), for details of the required construction of the electrodes and the test method to be used. It is recommended that electrical equipment energized from a grounded system not be used or operated by persons standing on the floor.

If waxes or other floor preservatives are used, they should have conductive qualities. Conductive floors may increase in resistance with age and therefore should be tested at regular intervals.

3.2.6.6 Conductive Footwear and Casters

When conductive flooring is used, operators or others entering the area must wear conductive nonsparking footwear. Mobile equipment should make contact with the floor directly or through conductive rubber casters. Their resistance should be checked at regular intervals or before entering the work area.

Shoe testers are available for determining the resistance while the shoes are being worn. Such testers are essentially direct-reading ohmmeters with resistors to limit the short-circuit current to 0.5 mA.

Where conductive floors and shoes are required, the resistance between the wearer and ground must not exceed 1 000 000 Ω, which is the total resistance of the conductive footwear on a person plus the resistance of the floor.

3.2.6.7 Special Precautions

In addition to the use of conductive floors and shoes, other controls may be considered, such as the following:

1) Providing wearing apparel with low static-producing qualities
2) Establishing rigid operating procedures
3) Using conductive rubber mats where conductive flooring is not used throughout an area

Hospital operating rooms utilize most of the preceding techniques because of the extreme hazard of anesthetic agents and the possibility of creating static electricity from nozzles, operators with improper attire, and other causes. The subject of dissipation of static electricity is well covered in ANSI/NFPA 77-1988 [10]. In industrial areas with extremely hazardous conditions, it may be well to consider these recommendations.

3.2.6.8 Proper Maintenance

Like other equipment, static control devices are no better than the maintenance they receive. Therefore, it is imperative that regularly scheduled inspections be made to perform the following checks:

1) Determine if all bonding and ground connections are intact.
2) Ascertain the resistance of all the equipment to ground. This may be found by the use of commercially available ohmmeters. A resistance of the order of 1 000 000 Ω is usually satisfactory for static mitigation.

3) Examine static neutralizers to be sure that they are in the correct position, and if of the high-voltage type, that they are energized and the points are clean.

4) Test belts to see if they have maintained their conducting characteristics.

5) Take resistance measurements of conductive flooring and footwear (see 3.2.6.5 and 3.2.6.6).

6) Take instrument readings to determine if static charges are accumulating, either because of the loss of one of the static control devices or because of a change in operating conditions, such as machine speed, the addition of material-handling equipment, or use of new materials that may have different characteristics.

3.2.7 Hazards in Various Facilities and Mechanisms, and Applicable Static Control Methods

3.2.7.1 General

A brief description of the particular hazards met within certain facilities and the methods of static control that are applicable is presented in the following paragraphs. A more complete discussion of many of these methods is given in the references that accompany these paragraphs.

3.2.7.2 Aviation Industry

Static charges are developed on aircraft both when they are in flight and when on the ground. The physical contact of the aircraft in flight with airborne particles such as dust, smoke, water particles, dry snow, and ice crystals will generate charges, and charged clouds in the proximity will also induce electrification in the aircraft. On the ground, a static charge can build up in the same manner as it does on any other rubber-tired vehicle when in motion or at rest. In addition, the movement of air and airborne particles over the large metallic surface of the aircraft, even though it is at rest, will also generate static, but of less magnitude.

Fire and explosions can occur during fueling operations because of static discharges if adequate bonding and grounding are not provided. Detailed recommendations for protecting against the hazard of static sparks during fueling operations are described in ANSI/NFPA 407-1988 [15], and the methods of providing suitable grounding facilities for static electricity in aircraft hangars are covered in ANSI/NFPA 409-1990 [16] and ANSI/NFPA 77-1988 [10].

3.2.7.3 Belted Drives

Most power belts and conveyor belts are constructed of insulating materials. These are pressed into contact with pulleys and idlers and generate static electricity at the point where the belt separates from the pulley. The generation of static electricity increases as speed increases or humidity decreases. Static generation will occur with either conducting or nonconducting pulleys. Rubber or leather fiat belts running at moderate or high speeds may generate sufficient static electricity to produce sparks. V belts are not as susceptible to hazardous static generation as are flat belts. Conveyor belts used for the transportation of solid material usually move at low speed, and usually do not produce static electricity. When conveyor belts carry heated or dry material, are operated in a heated atmosphere, or move with high velocity, static generation might be significant. In locations where static charges are a real hazard, considerations should be given to direct or gear drives rather than belted drives. If belted drives must be used, the following methods of static control should be used:

1) *A grounded static collector is installed.* This consists of a grounded piece of angle iron the width of the belt with metal spikes welded i in (25.4 mm) apart at the valley of the angle iron. The spikes do not project above the sides of the angle iron. The comb is installed within about 1/4 in (6.35 mm) of the belt 4–6 in (102–152 mm) beyond the point where the belt leaves both the driving and the driven pulleys, as shown in Fig 53. Such devices may sustain mechanical damage and are seldom used on power equipment. Tinsel bars used to remove static from wide sheet materials can also be used effectively with belts.

2) *A belt of conductive material is used.* These are available from belt manufacturers. A very important consideration in applying conductive rubber belts is to ensure that both the drive and the equipment are well grounded.

3) *Special belt dressings are applied.* This makes the inner surface of the belt conducting enough to leak the charges back to the pulley as fast as they are produced. Such dressings must be renewed frequently to be reliable.

4) When material transported by conveyor belts is spilled from the end of a belt into a hopper or chute, it may carry a static charge. The belt support and terminal pulleys should be electrically bonded to the hopper.

5) Metal pulleys are charged with an equal and opposite charge to that carried by the belt, and provisions should be made to transfer this charge to the earth through shaft, bearings, and equipment frame. When equipment frames are conductive, no charge is trapped. When wooden supports are used and are dried out by nearby heat, it is necessary to bond and ground the shaft and bearing to dissipate the trapped charges.

6) Sometimes the flow of static electricity through the oil film has resulted in sufficient roughening or pitting of the bearing surfaces to adversely affect the bearing life. In such a case it is necessary to bond the shaft to the bearing housing with some form of sliding metal or carbon brush to provide a low-resistance path between the shaft and the bearing housing. Where a bearing incorporates a nylon or other nonconductive bearing material, the shaft should be bonded as described above.

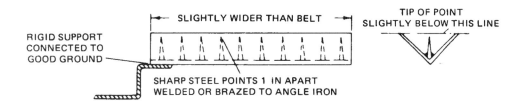

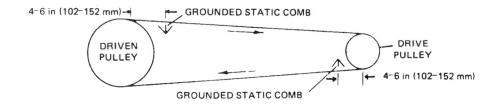

Figure 53—Details and Location of Static Comb*

*From Data Sheet 5–8, Static Electricity. © 1981 by Factory Mutual Engineering Corporation. Reprinted with permission.

One manufacturer of belts considers that a belt that shows a 10 000 000 Ω resistance when measured on an 8 1/2 in (216 mm) section will have sufficient static properties to make the belt safe throughout its life. Some feel that a much higher resistance will still permit dissipating static satisfactorily. However, it is desirable to keep the resistance as low as possible to provide a good margin of safety.

One method for testing, belts is to place two 5/8 inch (15.9 mm) in diameter electrodes on the belt 8 1/2 in (216 mm) apart. The electrodes should be moistened before being placed on the belt, and each should have 3 lb f/in^2 (20.7 kN/m^2) pressure applied. The resistance is then measured by means of a standard 500 V megohmmeter.

3.2.7.4 Coal Industry

Many explosions in coal mines and coal preparation plants have been attributed to the accumulation of coal dust and the movement of particles. More than ordinary precautions against the possibility of a static discharge spark, such as good maintenance, proper ventilation, and prevention of dust accumulation, must be taken to avoid such explosions. For a detailed study, refer to ANSI/NFPA 120-1988 [14] and ANSI/NFPA 85F-1988 [12].

3.2.7.5 Flour and Grain Industry

Material movement by means of conveyor belts, elevators, vacuums, blower systems, and other machinery of manufacture can be responsible for charge accumulation and the resulting static discharge. Fine particles of grain dust suspended in the air constitute an excellent explosive. Several explosions of grain elevators due to static sparks have been reported. For detailed information, refer to ANSI/NFPA 61B-1989 [7] and to ANSI/NFPA 61C-1989 [8].

Table 8 shows the minimum electrical energy required for the ignition of some dusts when in a cloud or in a layer (see ANSI/NFPA 77-1977 [10]).

3.2.7.6 Gas Processing

Gases that are not contaminated are unlikely to generate static electricity. Movement of a gas that is contaminated with metallic oxides, scale particles, or liquid particles can produce electrification.

Liquified petroleum gases behave in the same manner. Compressed air containing particles of condensed water vapor, liquid carbon dioxide, hydrogen gas containing particles of oxide, and steam when discharging from an orifice, can each produce static accumulation on the discharge device and the receiving object. This subject is covered in detail in ANSI/NFPA 77-1988 [10], ANSI/NFPA 58-1992 [4], ANSI/NFPA 59-1992 [5], ANSI/NFPA 59A-1990 [6], ANSI/NFPA 50A-1989 [2], and ANSI/NFPA 50B-1989 [3].

3.2.7.7 Paint Industry

The use of flammable solvents in paint-mixing operations represents a potential fire and explosion hazard due to ignition by static sparks which may be generated by the transferal of liquid from open containers by splash filling of tanks, by belt-driven machinery, and by the workers themselves.

3.2.7.8 Paper and Printing Industries

The movement of the paper itself over the various rolls and the machinery of manufacture tends to cause static voltages.

Where flammable inks and solvents are used in the process, charges thus produced have caused many fires and an occasional explosion. The static charge is also a source of trouble from the production standpoint. Sheets that become charged have an attraction for other objects, which causes difficulty in controlling the sheet, and the web may be torn. Also, the printed image may be damaged by the attraction of dust particles and loose paper fibers to the paper.

3.2.7.9 Refining Industry

The fire and explosion hazard due to static ignitions is well known in this industry, and extensive precautions against this hazard are necessary to safeguard lives and property. These are described in detail in [17].

3.2.7.10 Powder Processing

Most powders, when suspended as a dust cloud in air in sufficient concentration, are explosive, and some can be ignited by static sparks. Explosion venting of buildings and the equipment in which the materials are handled or processed may be necessary to minimize the damage if an explosion should occur, despite the usual precautions taken to prevent static accumulations. In the manufacture of explosives, the sensitivity to static ignitions varies with the material being processed. Primary explosives like fulminate of mercury can be detonated by a static spark.

Table 8—Minimum Electrical Energy for Ignition of Some Dust Clouds and Layers[*]

Material	Dust Cloud mJ	Dust Layer mJ
Alfalfa	320	—
Allyl alcohol resin	20	80.0
Aluminum	10	1.6
Aluminum stearate	10	40.0
Aryl sulfonyl hydrazine	20	160.0
Aspirin	25	160.0
Boron	60	—
Cellucotton	60	—
Cellulose acetate	10	—
Cinnamon	40	—
Coal, bituminous	60	560.0
Cocoa	100	—
Cork	35	—
Cornstarch	30	—
Dimethyl terephthalate	20	—
Dinitro toluamide	15	24.0
Ferromanganese	80	8.0
Gilsonite	25	4.0
Grain	30	—
Hexamethylenetetramine	10	—
Iron	20	7.0
Magnesium	20	0.24
Manganese	80	3.2
Methyl methacrylate	15	—
Nut shell	50	—
Paraformaldehyde	29	—
Pentaerythritol	10	—
Phenolic resin	10	40.0
Phthalic anhydride	15	—
Pitch	29	6.0
Polyethylene	30	—
Polystyrene	15	—
Rice	40	—
Seed (clover)	40	—
Silicon	80	2.4
Soap	60	3840.0
Soybean	50	40.0
Stearic acid	25	—

Table 8—Minimum Electrical Energy for Ignition of Some Dust Clouds and Layers[*] (Continued)

Material	Dust Cloud mJ	Dust Layer mJ
Sugar	30	—
Sulfur	15	1.6
Thorium	5	0.004
Titanium	10	0.008
Uranium	45	0.004
Urea resin	80	—
Vanadium	60	8.0
Vinyl resin	10	—
Wheat flour	50	—
Wood flour	20	—
Zinc	100	400.0
Zirconium	5	0.0004

*Data from the US Bureau of Mines.

3.2.7.11 Rubber Industry

Rubber cement containing a high percentage of naphtha is used in the manufacture of many rubber products. Static charges generated at many points in the process are a frequent source of ignition of the naphtha vapors. The maintenance of a relative humidity of 50% or more, in addition to bonding and grounding the various parts of the processing equipment and the use of static eliminators, is usually needed for adequate control of static electricity. Operators should also avoid the use of rubber-soled shoes to help avoid accumulating a charge on their bodies. Flammable liquids having low flash points should be handled in closed systems or closed containers as much as possible. When transferring flammable liquids from one open conductive container to another, the containers should be bonded together to maintain both at the same voltage and grounded to avoid any possibility of spark.

Rubber-coating machines are particularly susceptible to fires caused by the ignition of flammable vapors due to the discharge of static electricity generated by the movement of fabric over rolls and under spreader knives.

3.2.7.12 Textile Industry

The use of automatic cleaning systems for the prompt removal of lint from the atmosphere and from the machinery, in addition to modern air conditioning and precise control of humidity, has greatly reduced the fire hazard from static electricity. An occasional fire in a loom is attributed to static electricity, but grounding the machine frame and bonding all metal parts together and maintaining a relative humidity of 60% or more usually will eliminate the hazard.

3.2.7.13 Hospitals

Mixtures of air and certain anesthetics and the use of oxygen and oxygen-enriched atmospheres introduce fire, explosion, and electrical hazards. Areas where easily ignited anesthetic agents such as ethyl ether, cyclopropane, divinyl ether, trifluro ethyl ether, and ethylene are present should be thoroughly protected against the possibility of dangerous accumulations of static electricity that may cause ignition. The principal static safeguards in these areas include the following: conducting floors, use of metal or conductive material for all furnishings in direct contact with the floor; conductive shoes for personnel; prohibition of silk, wool, and synthetic garments in these areas unless used as hosiery or undergarments that are entirely in contact with the skin; maintenance of relative humidity at not less than 50%; and grounding of all exposed non—current-carrying metal parts of electrical equipment such as portable lamps, appliances, fixtures, cabinets, and cases, as required by ANSI/NFPA 70-1990 (the NEC) [9] (Article 517). For more complete coverage of the subject, see Chapter 12 of ANSI/NFPA 99-1990 [13].

In connection with the grounding of electrical equipment in these areas, more than ordinary care is needed for the maintenance of all electrical systems and equipment, because the electric-shock hazard is greatly increased due to the use of conductive shoes by personnel and the installation of conductive floors.

Recent developments indicate that the grounding of noncurrent-carrying metal enclosures generally required for electrical apparatus used in operating rooms and intensive care units, such as electrocardiographs, oscilloscopes,defibrillators, pacemakers, radios, television sets, vapor generators, and electrical cauterizing equipment, may be increasing the shock hazard to patients and personnel in these areas, due to leakage currents over the grounding conductor. Patients in intensive care units may be dangerously exposed. Transient leakage currents of as little as 20 μA over circuits for monitoring various physiological functions of a patient in an intensive care unit could be fatal where the probes are applied internally. To be safe, circuits should be designed so that leakage currents do not exceed 10 μA, according to some authorities. For more complete coverage of this subject, see the NEC [9], Article 517, and IEEE Std 602-1986 (ANSI) [19], Chapter 6.

3.2.7.14 Dry Cleaning

Dry cleaning is defined as the process of removing dirt, grease, paint, and other stains from wearing apparel, textile fabrics, rugs, etc., by the use of nonaqueous liquids (solvents). The various dry-cleaning methods include de the following:

1) Immersion and agitation in solvent in closed vessels
2) Brushing or scouring with cleaning solvents
3) Dual-phase processing

Dry-cleaning systems are divided into the following types:

Type I. Systems employing solvents having a flash point below 100 °F (37.8 °C)

Type II. Systems employing solvents having a flash point at or above 100 °F (37.8 °C) and below 140 °F (60 °C)

Type IIIA. Systems employing solvents having a flash point at or above 140 °F (60 °C), and below 200 °F (93.3 °C) and complying with the requirements of ANSI/NFPA-32-1990 [1], Chapter 3.

Type IIIB. Systems employing solvents having a flash point at or above 200 °F (93.3 °C) and complying with the requirements of ANSI/NFPA-32-1990 [1], Chapter 3.

Type IV. Systems using solvents that will not support combustion or are nonflammable at ordinary temperatures and only moderately flammable at higher temperatures, and complying with the requirements of ANSI/NFPA 32-1990 [1], Chapter 4.

Type V. Same as type IV, except they comply with the requirements of ANSI/NFPA 32-1990 [1], Chapter 5.

At the present time, the use of Type I systems is prohibited by ANSI/NFPA 32-1990 [1].

Storage tanks, treatment tanks, purifiers, pumps, piping, washers, extractors, drying tumblers, drying cabinets, combination units, and other similar apparatus should be bonded together. If this equipment is not grounded by virtue of its connection to the electric power service, it should be grounded.

Special consideration should be given to the control of static electricity in the handling of fabrics. When they are transferred from one piece of equipment to bonded together. Humidification of the area will also help to dissipate a static charge.

Personnel working in these areas and performing dry-cleaning operations can accumulate static charges, and the wearing of footwear that may insulate the person from ground should be avoided. Conductive floors, grounded metal work tables, and conductive footwear are helpful in removing such charges. For more details see ANSI/NFPA 32-1990 [1].

3.2.7.15 Offices

Business machines handling papers and plastic tapes, sheets, or cards often accumulate static charges. These may interfere with the operation of the machine by causing papers to stick together, attracting lint and dust particles, or transmitting minor shocks to the operators. The involuntary reflex action due to such discharges, though otherwise of no hazard, may sometimes result in injury to the personnel. Grounding of all non-current-carrying metal parts of the machine will prevent the accumulation of the charge, but curing the operational difficulties may necessitate the use of humidifiers or static neutralizers, whichever is most practical.

3.2.7.16 Video Display Terminals and Other Sensitive Electronic Equipment

(See Chapter 5.)

3.3 Lightning Protection Grounding

3.3.1 Nature of Lightning

3.3.1.1 General

Lightning is the discharging of high-voltage cells (usually negative) within clouds to each other or to the earth. These charged cells in clouds normally attract charges of opposite polarity on the surface of (or on high objects on) the earth directly below them. When the cell charge reaches a critical level (when the insulation between cloud and earth breaks down), it develops a stepped ionized path, frequently to the earth, resulting in a high current discharge (stroke) which neutralizes, for the moment, these cloud and earth charges. The discharge current increases from zero to a maximum in, usually, from 1 to 10 µs, then declines to half the peak value in from 20 to 1000 µs. Lightning strokes usually consist of several components. The original, rather slowly developing, component is followed, on the average, by three subsequent components. These subsequent components follow the original component by times of up to 0.5 s and are the result of the original charge center in the cloud being recharged by internal flashes from other charge centers in the cloud. These subsequent components develop much more rapidly than the original components, with rates of rise of from two to ten times that of the original component. Also, it has been found that the rate of rise is not linear, as it has generally been considered to be in the past, but exponential, with rate increasing rapidly in the last few tenths of a micro-second of rise time. This is important in aspects of lightning protection where the voltage to be guarded against is the product of the rate of current rise (di/dt) and the mutual inductance of a conductor in the magnetic field of a stroke location. The length of a conductor thus affected may exceed 2 mi. The maximum rate of rise of about 7% of subsequent component strokes exceeds 100 000 A/µs. Figure 54 shows relative rates. These multiple components provide the flickering appearance of lightning strokes. The average peak stroke current is about 40 000 A, although some stroke peak currents are as great as 270 000 A [24].

The point on which the lightning stroke terminates is frequently a point of some elevation, such as a tree, a building, a transmission line and its towers, or similar raised structures. This terminal may be on a metallic structure, which is a good current conductor, or it may be on something that is considered a semiconducting material. These include the following:

1) Trees with the moist cambium layer under the bark
2) Wooden structures with wetted surfaces, moisture residual within the timbers, or internal piping or wiring
3) Masonry structures with wetted surfaces or moisture tracks down the internal surface
4) Concrete structures with reinforcing material, possibly with sections not bonded together

These semiconducting paths are sufficiently conductive to permit the flow of *opposite-polarity* charges upward as the cloud cell approaches, but they are inadequate to permit the severe stroke current to flow without extreme heating or mechanical effects. This is due to high resistance in the path of discharge. Probably the most violent result is the explosive vaporization of any moisture, such as in the cambium layer of trees, or a moisture path in masonry buildings.

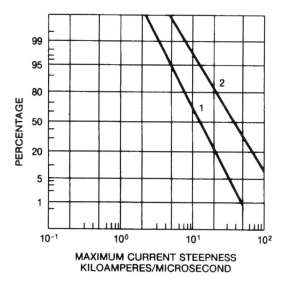

Figure 54—Cumulative Frequency Distribution of Maximum Rates of Rise of Lightning Currents (from Reference [23])
1. Negative First Strokes
2. Negative Subsequent Strokes

The bark is "exploded" off the tree, and stone and bricks are expelled by the steam pressure from the structure. At points where reinforcing elements are not interconnected, rupture of the intervening material results. Wood structural members simply explode from vaporization of the contained moisture. Light metal elements in the stroke path may be distorted by the magnetic stresses of the stroke current.

Probably an even greater danger results when flammable materials, such as petroleum or some chemical products, or in particular explosives, are subject to lightning stroke discharges. The temperature at the terminal of the stroke, or at any high-resistance point in the path over which the current flows en route to ground, is likely to ignite these materials.

Even when a stroke does not occur at a particular point but is completed to a nearby point on earth or another point within the cloud, the discharge of the cloud cell forces the immediate dissipation of the opposite charges on prominent points on the earth. The return to earth of these previously-bound charges, known as an induced stroke, may be several hundred amperes in magnitude and can be damaging to sensitive materials, such as flammables and explosives. Low-voltage electrical and instrument devices, too, are subject to damage from this source. Protection from induced strokes is conferred by the same means as for direct strokes.

Lightning can cause damage to structures by direct stroke and to electric equipment by surges coming in over exposed power lines [39]. Surges may be the result of direct strokes to the line at some distance away, or they may be electrostatically induced voltages. Damage due to direct stroke can be minimized by providing a direct path of low resistance to earth.

3.3.1.2 Need for Protection

Damage to structures and equipment due to the surge effect is a subject in itself, and protection against this type of damage is not within the scope of this section, except as grounding is involved. Refer to ANSI/NFPA 78-1989 [11] for means of protection.

It is not possible to positively protect a structure against damage from direct stroke, except by completely enclosing it with metal.

It is, however, rare that protection against lightning is really required for all objects or structures at a given site or installation. A number of factors require consideration in determining the extent to which lightning protection should be provided or whether this protection is really needed:

1) Personnel hazards
2) Possible production loss, including overhead and indirect losses
3) Possible damage, and repair cost
4) Effect on insurance premiums
5) Value and nature of structure or its contents
6) Thunderstorm frequency (isokeraunic maps, Figs 55 and 56)
7) Number and severity of lightning strokes per storm (average)
8) Cost of protection

The above factors are listed in approximate order of importance. In certain situations this order may change. The number of days per year with thunderstorms occurring in a given region is known as the keraunic level of that region. The isokeraunic maps of the United States and Canada are shown in Figs 55 and 56. There are, however, local variations, dependent on topography, mineral content, and moisture content, which these maps do not take into account. Also, there are areas where such storms are more intense, and other locations where there are more storms per year, so Figs 55 and 56 need to be modified to give consideration to these local variations.

Relying on isokeraunic maps to determine lightning stroke frequency introduces some inaccuracies. A "thunderstorm day" is defined as any day during which thunder is heard at the reporting point. No information is included concerning duration or intensity of the storm, its distance or direction from the reporting point, or whether the lightning discharges are intra-cloud or cloud-to-ground. Several recent studies, such as [25], [33], and [35], have reported on programs to actually measure the frequency and severity of cloud-to-ground strokes over broad geographic areas. While there does not appear to be enough information available yet to use these data to replace traditional isokeraunic maps, further development of these detection systems should yield more accurate lightning-stroke density data than is presently available from the isokeraunic maps. Figure 57 is a contour map of mean annual lightning strike density, taken from Reference [33].

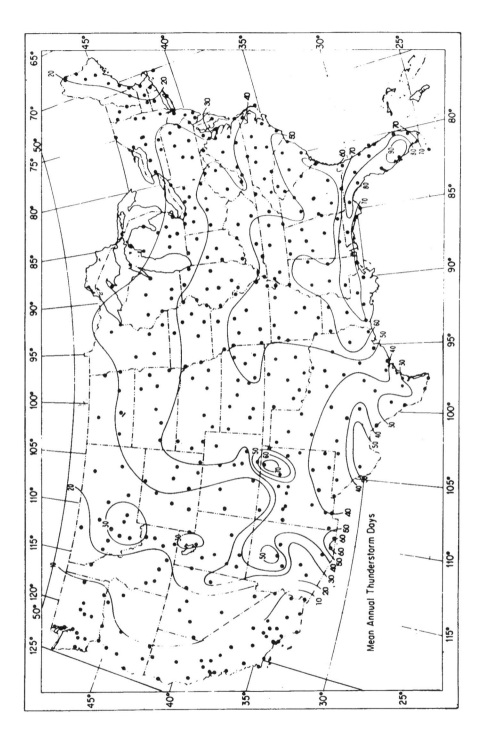

**Figure 55—Annual Isokeraunic Map of the Continental United States,
Showing Mean Annual Number of Days with Thunderstorms**

The highest frequency is encountered in south-central Florida. Since 1894, the recording of thunderstorms has been
defined as the local calendar days during which thunder was heard. A day with thunderstorms is so recorded,
regardless of the number of occurring on that day. The occurrence of lighting without thunder us not recorded as a
thunderstorm. (Map from reference [33].)

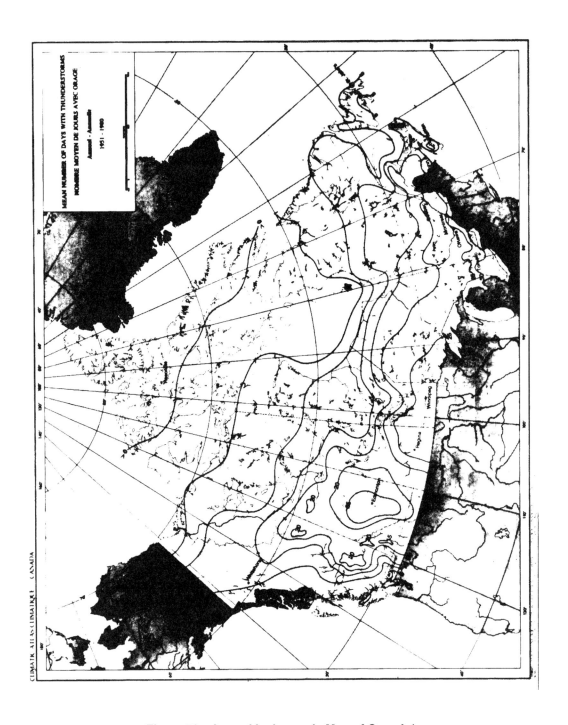

Figure 56—Annual Isokeraunic Map of Canada*
*Data based on the period of 1957–1972. Data from Meteorological Division, Department of Transportation, Canada.

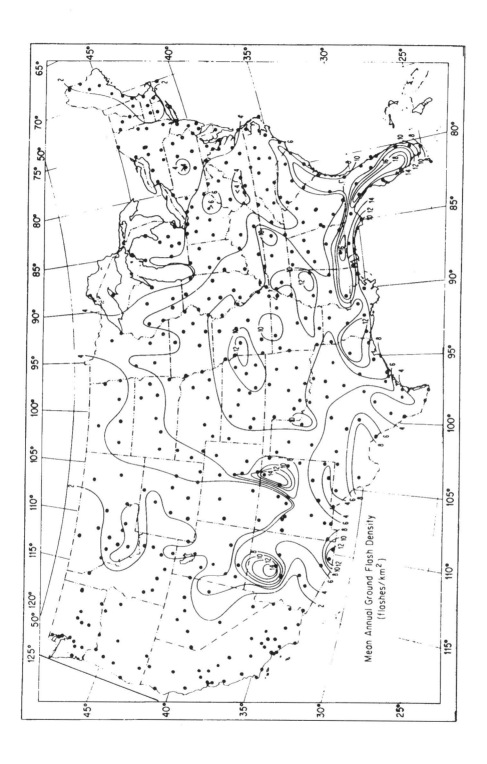

**Figure 57—Contour Map of Mean Annual Lightning Strike Density
(Map from Reference [32])**

Appendix I of ANSI/NFPA 78-1989 [11] contains a *risk assessment guide* that provides guidelines on the need for lightning protection.

3.3.2 Equipment and Structures to Be Considered

Equipment and structures can be separated into five classifications for their need of lightning protection.

1) The first class needs very little or no additional protection. The only real requirements for these is that they be effectively connected to a suitable grounding electrode. This class includes:
   a) All metal structures except tanks or other enclosures of flammable materials
   b) Water tanks, silos, and similar structures, constructed largely of metal
   c) Flagpoles made of conductive material
2) The second class consists of buildings with conducting surfaces and nonconducting framework, such as metal-roofed and metal-clad buildings. This type requires the addition of down conductors to connect the exterior roof and cladding to suitable grounding electrodes.
3) The third class consists of metal-framed buildings with nonconducting facings. These need the addition of conducting air terminals suitably located, connected to the frame, and projecting beyond and above the facing to act as the lightning terminal points, eliminating puncture of the facing.
4) The fourth class consists of nonmetallic structures, either framing or facing. These require extensive protection treatment. Included are:
   a) Buildings of wood, stone, brick, tile, or other nonconducting materials, without metal reinforcing members.
   b) High stacks and chimneys. Even with reinforcing members, these should have full lightning-protection treatment of air terminals, down conductors, and grounding electrodes.
5) A fifth class consists of items of high risk or loss consequences, which normally receive full lightning-protection treatment, including air terminals or diverters, down conductors, and grounding electrodes (see 3.3.3.2). These include:
   a) Buildings of great aesthetic, historical, or intrinsic value
   b) Buildings containing readily combustible or explosive materials
   c) Structures containing substances that would be dangerous if released by the effects of a lightning stroke
   d) Tanks and tank farms
   e) Power plants and water pumping stations
   f) Transmission lines
   g) Power stations and substations

Public service facilities such as power plants and pumping stations provide extremely important functions, and thus must always be protected adequately.

3.3.3 Requirements for Good Protection

3.3.3.1 Protection Principles

Lightning cannot be prevented; it can only be intercepted or diverted to a path that will, if well designed and constructed, not result in damage. Even this means is not positive, providing only 99.5–99.9% protection. Complete protection can be provided only by enclosing the object in a complete metal (or metal mesh) encapsulation. For example, a person in a metal-topped, closed automobile is safe from lightning stroke injury. Still, a 99.5% protection level will reduce the incidence of direct strokes from one stroke per 30 years [normal in the keraunic level of 30 for a 100 ft (30 m) square, 30 ft (9.1 m) high structure] to one stroke per 6000 years, while 99.9% protection will reduce the incidence to one stroke per 30 000 years. Protection at 99.5% is the practical choice. The fundamental theory of lightning protection of structures is to provide means by which a discharge may enter or leave the earth without passing through paths of high resistance. Such a condition is usually met by grounded steel-frame structures. Suitable protection is nearly always provided by the installation of air terminals, down conductors, and grounding electrodes.

It should be noted that the use of air terminals on a building or structure may increase the frequency of lightning strokes at that specific location. Although the building may be protected by a properly installed lightning-protection system, the increased stroke frequency may have a detrimental effect on processes or operations within the building.

In the case of metal-frame buildings, the multiplicity of closed conducting loops within the structure will act to resist the transmission of surge voltages into the interior of the building. A direct lightning stroke to an upper level of such a metal building would lead to a surface curtain of surge-current flow traveling downward toward the ground on the outer ring of vertical conducting columns of the building. Any tendency for a surge current to flow toward the building center is at once blocked by an induced current around the closed metal conducting frame. The inductive voltage drop associated with this vertical surface shell of surge current is associated with a magnetic field encircling the entire building structure. Such a magnetic field encircles every other vertical conducting member within the building, and induces an equal voltage between the top and bottom of each column. Thus, there is minimal tendency for any one vertical conducting path up through the building to display a voltage difference to any other internal vertical path. Even though a lightning stroke has caused the top deck of the building to go 250 kV above ground, almost none of this voltage appears as a *difference* voltage between different conducting paths at the top deck of the building.

Lightning exposure external to a metal-frame structure, including direct hits to the structure, presents almost no surge-voltage protection problem to electric power circuits and electric power equipment contained entirely within the *shell* of the structure. (Sensitive electronic equipment, such as computers, may require a higher level of protection. (See Chapter 5 for recommendations for the protection of sensitive electronic equipment.)

The protection of electrical equipment and overhead distribution lines from the effects of lightning is not within the scope of this section. The modern techniques used for line protection, however, are very similar to the principles of protection for buildings, tanks, and nonelectrical objects.

Until very recently, criteria used to determine the lightning-protection zone depended on the principle of a linear-sided *cone* of protection from high masts or overhead wires. The angle of protection surface from the horizontal varied from 45° for important structures to 30° for those of lesser importance. These angles were to be used without regard to the height above ground. These criteria were found to be inadequate, particularly for objects more than 75 ft (22.86 m) high. Actually, very tall objects, such as radio and television towers and very tall buildings, were found to be struck below their tops by stroke paths coming from the side, although the top of the structure was properly protected against the lightning.

In place of the linear-sided cone of protection, a curved-sided zone of protection has been found applicable. This concept, first developed by Lee (see References [30] and [31]), has been adopted in recent editions of the Lightning Protection Code [11]. The zone of protection is defined by a sphere with a radius of 150 ft (45 m), tangent to the earth or nearby grounded objects and touching a protecting grounded (overhead) member or a lightning protection air terminal. Rotating this sphere horizontally through 360° defines a surface, and the area below this surface is the zone of protection. The surface of a zone of protection is also formed when such a sphere is resting on two or more air terminals. Objects within this zone have protection from 99.5% of direct strokes. It is necessary to analyze the zone of protection for all directions around a structure to be protected, not just one side. Corners particularly require protection, since these have been found to be favorite targets for lightning stroke termination. See References [11], [30], [31], and [34] for further information.

3.3.3.2 Practices for Direct Protection

Fundamentally, direct lightning protection (lightning-protection systems) consists of placing air terminals or diverter elements suitably at the top of the structure to be protected, and connecting them by adequate down conductors to grounding electrodes (earth). An air terminal, as defined in ANSI/NFPA 78-1989 [11], is "that component of a lightning-protection system that is intended to intercept lightning flashes." A necessary principle is that the adequate down conductor should not include any high-resistance or high-reactance portions or connections and should present the least possible impedance to earth. There should be no sharp bends or loops. Steel-framed structures, adequately grounded, meet these requirements with only the provision for terminating the stroke on a metallic air terminal, connected to the frame structure, to avoid the possibility of puncturing any roofing or siding to reach the frame. In the absence of a steel framework, a down conductor providing at least two paths to earth for a stroke to any air terminal is generally adequate. The contact surfaces at the joints of structural steel buildings, which rely on the building steel for the path to ground, should not be painted with an electrically nonconducting paint. Where nonconductive paints are used, the joints should be jumpered or separate down conductors should be installed.

Air terminals attached to the structure itself are pointed solid rods or pipes, at least 10 in (0.25 m) long to possibly 20 ft (6.1 m) long. These air terminals are separated by distances determined through use of the *critical radius* described in [30], [31], [34], so that the structure surface surface will not protrude through or beyond the surface of protection.

The Lightning Protection Code, ANSI/NFPA 78-1989 [11], gives detailed instructions for the placement and spacing of air terminals on roofs of buildings of various configurations and on structures other than roofed buildings. In general, on the perimeter of a building with a fiat or gently sloping roof, 10 in (0.25 m) terminals should not be separated more than 20 ft (6.1 m), and 2 ft (0.61 m) terminals should not be separated more than 25 ft (7.6 m). On roof areas within the perimeter, spacing of 50 ft (15.2 m) will suffice. This code also requires air terminals to be secured against overturning, and it requires air terminals over 24 in (0.61 m) to be supported at a point not less than one half its height. Since the Lightning Protection Code [11] has been adopted by ordinance in many jurisdictions, it should be consulted for detailed requirements by any engineer designing a lightning-protection system.

All air terminals should be connected by down conductors and should form a two-way path from each air terminal to make connection to the grounding electrode (voltages double at an open circuit or end, in a lightning down conductor). Bend radii should be as long as possible, not less than 8 in (20 cm), since sharp bends increase the reactance of the conductor. Reactance is much more important than resistance because of the very high frequency of the surge front. At least two down conductors should be provided on all structures, except that only one down conductor is needed for masts, spires, and flagpoles.

The location of down conductors will depend on the location of the air terminals, the size of the structure being protected, the most direct routing, the security against damage or displacement, the location of metallic bodies, water pipes, the grounding electrode, and the ground conditions. If the structure has electrically continuous metallic columns, these columns will act as down conductors. The air terminals must be interconnected by conductors to make connection with the columns. The average distance between down conductors should not exceed 100 ft (30 m). Irregularly shaped structures may require extra down conductors. Down conductors passing through runways, driveways, playgrounds, public walks, etc., should be guarded to prevent their damage or displacement. If a down conductor is run through ferrous metal tube or pipe, the conductor must be bonded at both ends of the tube or pipe.

Every down conductor must be connected, at its base, to an earthing or grounding electrode. This electrode needs to be not less than 2 ft (0.61 m) away from the base of the building and should extend below the building foundation if possible. The length of the grounding conductor is highly important. A horizontal run of, say, 50 ft (15.2 m) to a better electrode (such as a water pipe) is much less effective than a connection to a driven rod alongside the structure itself. Electrodes should make contact with the earth from the surface downward to avoid flashing at the surface. Earth connections should be made at uniform intervals about the structure, avoiding as much as possible the grouping of connections on one side. Properly made connections to earth are an essential feature of a lightning-rod system for the protection of buildings (see Chapter 4).

Naturally, the greater the number of down conductors and grounding electrodes, the lower will be the voltage developed within the protection system, and the better it will perform. This is one of the great advantages of the steelframed building. It has as many down conductors as it has columns, or one about every 15 ft (4.57 m). Also, at the bottom of each column it has a footing, which is a very effective electrode (see Chapter 4).

Interior metal parts of a non-metal-framed building that are near a down conductor may need to be connected to that down conductor. Otherwise, they may sustain side flashes from it; these occur because of a voltage drop in the lower portion of that down conductor and electrode. Reference [11] includes formulas for determining whether this bonding is required. The same is true for the juxtaposition of interior metal parts and exterior metal roofing or sheathing. Exterior emergency ladders should also be bonded to the nearest down conductor. On a flat-top building protected by air terminals, all metallic parts and equipment projecting higher than the air terminals, such as airconditioning and heating equipment, should be bonded to the lightning-protection system. Metal less than 3/16 in (4.76 mm) thick should have an air terminal mounted on top.

For high-rise buildings and towers, an equalizing horizontal bonding loop should be installed at approximately every 60 ft (18 m). This bonding loop should be connected at every down conductor to equalize the voltage differences between down conductors. If this is not done, during severe lightning strokes, a voltage will appear between down conductors as the surge impedance of each down conductor is different, causing high voltage gradients between these down conductors. These equalizing loops become more important if the structure area is small since in this case there are fewer down conductors to carry the total stroke current.

Very tall structures, such as those exceeding 1000 ft (305 m), should be equipped with horizontal exterior air terminals bonded to the down conductors and the horizontal bonding; loops. At elevations below 1500 ft (457 m), the horizontal air terminals should be spaced no further apart than 120 ft (36 m) vertically, or at every other horizontal bonding loop. Above 1500 ft (457 m), the horizontal air terminals should be installed every 60 ft (18 m) vertically or at every horizontal bonding loop. These terminals are needed because of two natural attributes of lightning. First, it is possible for an electrified cloud to exist; at an altitude as low as 1500 ft (457 m), so that the top of a tall structure may be in the cloud. Second, a lightning stroke develops as a rapid series of short segments, not as a single continuous breakdown. The direction of any single segment is somewhat unpredictable. It is therefore possible for a stroke to pass the top of a tall structure, then strike sideways to some part of the structure below the top. The horizontal air terminals provide protection to metallic items, such as window frames, that might otherwise be the terminating point of lightning strokes from either of these two sources.

3.3.4 Practices for Lightning Protection

3.3.4.1 General

Buildings and structures involving hazardous liquids, gases, or explosives require additional protection. In these, it is highly desirable to keep the stroke current away from the structure, not even utilizing its metal skin or framework as a down conductor. For such cases, including tanks, tank farms, and explosive manufacture and storage, a separate diverter protection system is employed.

The diverter element consists of one or more masts, or one or more elevated wires (between masts or poles), meeting the requirements of lightning protection [11]. For structures containing flammable liquids and gases, the radius of the sphere of protection is reduced to 100 ft (30 m), instead of the 150 ft (45 m) dimension normally used. To prevent sideflashes, the minimum distance between a mast or overhead ground wire and the structure to be protected should not be less than the sideflash distance as described in Reference [11]. (See Fig 58.) Metal masts may act as grounding conductors. Wood poles should have an air terminal securely mounted to the top of the pole, and a copper or copperweld conductor along the pole should be provided as grounding conductor. The guy wires for an elevated wire span can be designed to serve as grounding conductors. As with all other types of grounding conductors, suitable earthing electrodes are necessary.

3.3.4.2 Tanks and Tank Farms

In some places it is not considered necessary to protect tanks containing flammable liquids or gases from lightning, provided that the base of the tanks are adequately grounded. Direct strokes are permitted to the tank top or walls, and as long as the steel is 3/16 in (4.76 mm) or more in thickness, there is little danger of a stroke puncturing it. Steel tanks with steel roofs and floating metal roofs are generally considered to be self-protecting. Tanks with nonmetallic roofs are not self-protecting and should usually be protected with air terminals, conducting masts, or elevated ground wires. In all cases, joints and piping connections should be electrically continuous, and all vapor or gas openings closed or flame-proof. The possibility of a direct stroke to the vicinity of a vent or leak is taken care of by an air terminal of suitable length [30], [31], [34].

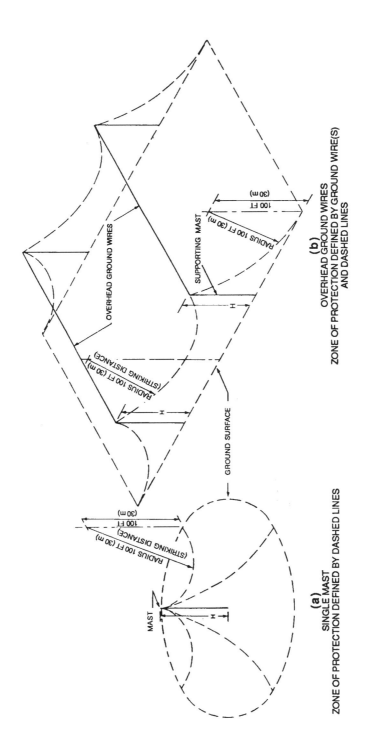

Figure 58—Lightning Protection for Structures Containing Hazardous Materials*

*Reprinted with permission from NFPA 78-1989, *Lighting Protection Code*, Copyright © 1989, National Fire Protection Association, Quincy, MA 02269. This reprinted materials is not the complete and official position of the National Fire Protection Association, on the referenced subject which is represented only by the standard in its entirety.

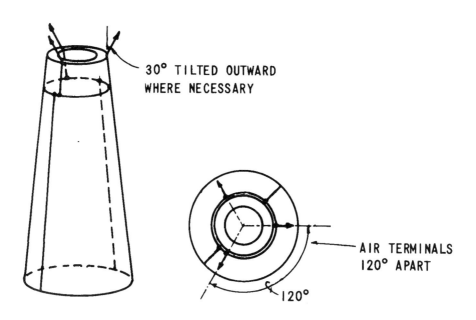

30° TILTED OUTWARD
WHERE NECESSARY

AIR TERMINALS
120° APART

120°

Figure 59—Lightning Protection for Stacks

3.3.4.3 Nonconducting Heavy-Duty Stacks

For heavy-duty stacks, including those in petroleum and chemical plants, air terminals, connected to a loop conductor around the top of the stack, and at least two down conductors to grounding electrodes at the base of the stack are required. (See Fig 59.) Air terminals should be made of solid copper or stainless steel and should be uniformly distributed around the top of cylindrical stacks at intervals not exceeding 8 ft (2.44 m). On square or rectangular stacks, air terminals should be located not more than 2 ft (0.61 m) from the corners and should be spaced not more than 8 ft (2.44 m) apart around the perimeter. Where the stack gas is nonflammable, the length of the terminals may be as little as 18 in (0.46 m). Where ventilating stacks emit explosive gas or dust, the length of the air terminals should be not less than 5 ft (1.52 m). Where the gas or dust is explosive and under forced draft, the length should be not less than 15 ft (4.57 m). In the latter case, tilting the terminals outward at 30 from the vertical is desirable.

Where the effluent is corrosive, as in flue gas, 1/16 in (1.6 mm) thick lead coating on the air terminals is required. The loop is also kept below the top of the stack.

3.3.4.4 Steeples

Steeples are similar to stacks except that they normally are sharp peaked and thus require only one air terminal. This should project far enough above the top ornamentation to meet the requirements of lightning protection. Otherwise, multiple air terminals or a multipointed terminal should be used to provide equivalent protection.

Steeples are frequently framed with wood, not metal, so adequate down conductors are a basic requirement.

3.3.4.5 High Masts

Equipment on the sides of very high masts, such as television or FM antennas, can be protected from direct stroke damage by the addition of lateral spikes or *thorns* projecting outward from the sides of the mast. At heights above the critical radius of 150 ft (45 m) [30], [31], [34], spikes in a horizontal or near-horizontal position, suitably spaced as described in [30], [31], [34], will cause strokes coming from the side to terminate on the spikes rather than on the mast itself. This will greatly reduce the possibility of damage to electrically fragile components by the termination of the lightning stroke arc. The number of spikes around the mast (three, four, five, or six), the length of the spikes, and their vertical spacing along the mast need to be determined for optimum economics, following the principles of lightning protection. Where masts are installed on top of a building, the bottom of the mast structure must be bonded at least at two points with the building grounding network.

3.3.4.6 Power Stations and Substations

Stations and substations require protection from direct strokes, obtainable using the circular-sided protection zone guidance set forth in [30], [31], [34]. Masts or overhead wires, or both, may be used. The grounding of these to the usually very adequate grounding network of the station or substation is, of course, necessary.

Protection of the attached overhead lines by means of an overhead grounded conductor or diverter (static wire) for 2000 ft (610 m) away from the station or substation is recommended. This will preclude direct strokes on this section of the line and will reduce the duty on the station surge arresters. The spacing of this overhead grounded conductor or diverter and its down conductors from the phase conductors must not be less than the basic impulse insulation level of the lightning-protection system. Otherwise, sideflashes to the phase conductors will occur, causing unnecessary outages. Generally, unless the lines are 66 kV or higher, it is not practical to install these overhead grounded conductors above them.

However, overhead grounded conductors may be desirable on some power lines below 66 kV, depending on past experience with such lines operating in high keraunic levels. To attain the desired protection, separation of phase conductors from one another and from the grounding down conductors must be raised to levels similar to those applicable to 66 kV and higher voltage systems. This frequently assumes positioning of the phase conductors on standoff insulators on one side of the pole, with the grounding down conductor offset on fiberglass standoff members on the opposite side of the pole. In this way, separations of about 5 ft (1.52 m) are readily available.

Lightning protection of power stations and substations includes the protection of station equipment by means of surge arresters [39]. These arresters should be mounted on, or closely connected to, the frames of the principal equipment that they are protecting, especially transformers (Fig 60). They may also be mounted on the steel framework of the station or substation where all components are closely interconnected by means of the grounding grid. For satisfactory lightning protection, substation grounding network resistance must not exceed 5 Ω for large stations, lower values are desirable.

The surge-arrester grounding conductor should be connected into the common station ground bus. As with lightning down conductors, the grounding conductor for surge arresters must be as short and straight as possible. The NEC [9], Article 280, requires that it be not less than AWG 6 (4.11 mm) for circuits of 1 kV and over, but larger sizes may be desirable to resist possible mechanical damage, corrosion, etc.

Figure 60—Typical Method of Grounding Surge Arrester

3.4 References

[1] ANSI/NFPA 32-1990, Dry Cleaning Plants.[12]

[2] ANSI/NFPA 50A-1989, Gaseous Hydrogen Systems at Consumer Sites.

[3] ANSI/NFPA 50B-1989, Liquefied Hydrogen Systems at Consumer Sites.

[4] ANSI/NFPA 58-1992, Storage and Handling of Liquefied Petroleum Gases.

---

[12]ANSI/NFPA publications can be obtained from the Sales Department, American National Standards Institute, 1430 Broadway, New York, NY 10018, or from Publication Sales, National Fire Protection Association, Batterymarch Park, Quincy, MA 02269, USA,

[5] ANSI/NFPA 59-1992, Storage and Handling of Liquefied Petroleum Gases at Utility Gas Plants.

[6] ANSI/NFPA 59A-1990, Production, Storage and Handling of Liquefied Natural Gas (LNG).

[7] ANSI/NFPA 61B-1989, Prevention of Fire and Dust Explosions in Grain Elevators and Handling Bulk Raw Agricultural Commodities..

[8] ANSI/NFPA 61C-1989, Fire and Dust Explosion in Feed Mills.

[9] ANSI/NFPA 70-1990, National Electrical Code.

[10] ANSI/NFPA 77-1988, Static Electricity.

[11] ANSI/NFPA 78-1989, Lightning Protection Code.

[12] ANSI/NFPA 85F-1988 Installation and Operation of Pulverized Fuel Systems.

[13] ANSI/NFPA 99-1990, Health Care Facilities.

[14] ANSI/NFPA 120-1988, Coal Preparation Plants.

[15] ANSI/NFPA 407-1988, Aircraft Fuel Servicing.

[16] ANSI/NFPA 409-1990, Aircraft Hangars.

[17] API-RP-2003 1991, Fifth Edition, Recommended Practice for Protection Against Ignitions Arising out of Static, Lightning, and Stray Currents.[13]

[18] IEC Publication 664, Insulation Coordination Within Low-Voltage Systems Including Clearances and Creepage Distances for Equipment. Geneva, Switzerland: International Electrotechnical Commission, 1980.[14]

[19] IEEE 602-1986, Recommended Practice for Electric Systems in Health Care Facilities (IEEE White Book) (ANSI).[15]

[20] Beach, R. Electrostatic Hazards and Their Control.

[21] Beach, R. "Grounding Principles and Practice—V: Static Electricity in Industry," in *Electrical Engineering*, vol 64, May 1945, pp. 184–194.

[22] Beach, R. "Industrial Fires and Explosions from Electrostatic Origin," in *Mechanical Engineering*, April 1953.

[23] Berger, K, Anderson, R. B., and Kroninger, H. "Parameters of Lightning Flashes," in *Electra*, vol. 40, pp. 101–119, 1975.

[24] Davis, N.H. Lightning Protection Systems. *NFPA Fire Protection Handbook*, 15th ed, chap 12.

[25] De La Rosa, F. and Velazquez, R. "Review of Ground Flash Density Measuring Devices Regarding Power System Applications," in *IEEE Transactions on Power Delivery*, vol. PRWD-4, no. 2, Apr. 1989.

---

[13] API publications are available from the Publications Section, American Petroleum Institute, 1200 L Street NW, Washington, DC 20005, USA.

[14] IEC publications are available from IEC Sales Department, Case Postale 131, 3 rue de Varembé, CH 1211, Genève 20, Switzerland/Suisse. IEC publications are also available in the United States from the Sales Department, American National Standards Institute, 11 West 42nd Street, 13th Floor, New York, NY 10036, USA.

[15] IEEE publications are available from the Institute of Electrical and Electronics Engineers, Service Center, 445 Hoes Lane, P.O. Box 1331, Piscataway, NJ 08855-1331, USA.

[26] Eichel, F. G. "Electrostatics," in *Chemical Engineering*. Mar 13, 1967.

[27] Gally, S. K ."Elements of Static Electricity," in *Gas*, Mar 1949, pp 42–46.

[28] Harper, W. R. *Contact and Frictional Electrification*. New York: Oxford University Press, 1967.

[29] Klinkenberg, A., and Van Der Minne, J. L. *Electrostatics in the Petroleum Industry*. New York: Elsevier Publishing Company, 1958.

[30] Lee, R. H. "Protection Zone for Buildings Against Lightning Strokes Using Transmission Line Protection Practice," in *IEEE Transactions on Industry Applications*, vol. IA-14, Nov./Dec. 1978.

[31] Lee, R. H. "Lightning Protection of Buildings," in *IEEE Transaction on Industry Applications*, vol. IA-15, May/June 1979.

[32] Loeb, L. B. "The Basic Mechanisms of Static Electrification," in Science, Dec. 7, 1945, pp. 573–576.

[33] Macgorman, D. R., Maker, M. W., and Rust, W. D. *Lightning Strike Density for Contiguous United States from Thunderstorm Duration Records*. NUREG Report CR-3759. Washington, DC: U.S. Government Printing Office, 1984.

[34] Offermann, P. F. "Lightning Protection of Structures," in *Conference Record of the 1969 Fourth Annual Meeting of the IEEE Industry and General Applications Group, 69C5-IGA*.

[35] Orville, R. E. and Songster, H. "The East Coast Lightning Detection Network," in *IEEE Transactions on Power Delivery*, vol. PRWD-2, no. 3, July 1987.

[36] Pearson, J. M. "Protection Against Static Electricity," in *Automotive Transactions*, vol. 21, 1940.

[37] "Static Electricity," in *Handbook of Industrial Loss Prevention*. Factory Mutual Engineering Corporation, 1968, chap. 30.

[38] "Static Electricity," Circular C-438, National Bureau of Standards, Boulder, CO. Washington, DC: United States Government Printing Office.

[39] Walsh, G. W. A Review of Lightning Protection and Grounding Practices. *IEEE Transactions on Industry Applications*, vol. IA-9, Mar./Apr. 1973.

3.5 Bibliography

Beach, R. "Mechanical Electrostatic Neutralizer Discharge and Safety Characteristics," in *Mechanical Engineering*, vol. 71, pp 329—334.

IEC 1024-1, first edition, 1990-03, Protection of Structures Against Lightning, Part 1: General Principles.

Hedlund, C. F. "Lightning Protection for Buildings," in *IEEE Transactions on Industry and General Applications*, vol IGA-3, Jan./Feb. 1967, pp 26–30.

Hughes, J. F., and Bright, A. W. "Electrostatic Hazards Associated with Power Handling in Silo Installations," in *IEEE Transactions on Industry Applications*, vol. IA-15, Jan./Feb.1979.

Lewis, B., and Von Elbe, G. *Combustion, Flames and Explosions*. New York: Academic Press, 1951.

Chapter 4

Connection to Earth

4.1 Resistance to Earth

4.1.1 Nature of Grounding Resistance

The grounding resistance of an electrode is made up of:

1) Resistance of the (metal) electrode
2) Contact resistance between the electrode and the soil
3) Resistance of the soil, from the electrode surface outward, in the geometry set up for the flow of current outward from the electrode to infinite earth

The first two resistances are or can be made small with respect to the third (fraction of an ohm) and can be neglected for all practical purposes. The third element is the one to be discussed here.

As the earth is (relatively) infinite in its size compared to the grounding systems as we know them, so too is its capacity to absorb a virtually unlimited supply of current. Practically, however, this unlimited current to the earth is transmitted across the metal electrode-earth soil interface in a way that is best described as follows:

Around a grounding electrode, the resistance of the soil is the sum of the series resistances of virtual shells of earth, located progressively outward from the rod. The shell nearest the rod has the smallest circumferential area or cross section, so it has the highest resistance. Successive shells outside this one have progressively larger areas, and thus progressively lower resistances. As the radius from the rod increases, the incremental resistance per unit of radius decreases effectively to nearly zero.

To help visualize this, Fig 61 shows a typical 10 ft (3 m) by 5/8 in (16 ram) ground rod in soil. The path of ground current outward from the rod surface consists of successive cylindrical and hemispherical shells. As the distance from the rod increases, so do the cross-sectional areas of the individual shells. As their areas increase, their individual series resistances decrease inversely with the area. Table 9 shows the result of carrying out this calculation based on the distance of 25 ft (7.62 m) representing 100% of the total earth resistance. The table shows that in the first 0.1 ft (0.03 m) away from the rod surface, 25% of the total resistance is incurred. In the first 0.5 ft (0.15 m) and 1.0 ft (0.3 m), 52 and 68%, respectively, of the total resistance is incurred.

Therefore, it is shown that the first few inches away from the rod are the most important ones, as far as reducing the electrode resistance is concerned. In high-soil-resistivity locations, decreasing the soil resistivity in this area, such as by chemical treatment or the use of concrete, will be most useful in improving the effectiveness of a grounding-electrode system.

Adding more electrodes to the first one, in order to reduce the resistance, does not affect the resistance much if close to the first electrode. Multiple electrodes closely spaced do not have a resistance reciprocally proportional to their number. The nonreciprocity is caused by the common mutual resistance in which the current of each raises the voltage of the other. Since the voltage is higher for the same current flow, the resistance is increased by the mutual resistance.

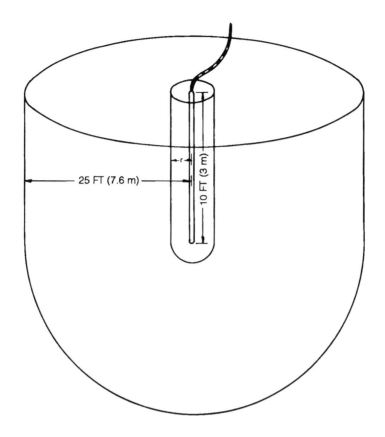

Figure 61—Electrode Resistance Development

Table 9—Electrode Resistance at a Radius r ft from a 10 ft (3 m) Long by 5/8 in (16 mm) Diameter Rod (Where Total Resistance at r = 25 ft (7.6 m) = 100%)

| Distance from Electrode Surface (r) | | Approximate Percentage of Total Resistance |
ft	m	
0.1	0.03	25
0.2	0.06	38
0.3	0.09	46
0.5	0.15	52
1.0	0.3	68
5.0	1.5	86
10.0	3.0	94
15.0	4.6	97
20.0	6.1	99
25.0	7.6	100
(100.0)*	30.5	(104)
(1000.0)*	305.0	(117)

*These figures show that for the most practical reasons the majority of the resistance to remote earth occurs within 25 ft of the electrode, i.e., at 1000 ft the resistance is only 17% higher than that of 25 ft.

4.1.2 Recommended Acceptable Values

The most elaborate grounding system may not perform satisfactorily unless the connection of the system to earth is adequate for the particular installation. It follows, therefore, that the earth connection is one of the most important parts of the whole grounding system. It is also the most difficult part to design.

The connection to earth or the electrode system, needs to have a sufficiently low resistance to help permit prompt operation of the circuit protective devices in the event of a ground fault, to provide the required safety from shock to personnel who may be in the vicinity of equipment frames, enclosures, conductors, or the electrodes themselves and to limit transient overvoltages.

ANSI/NFPA 70-1990 (the NEC) [1],[16] for example, stipulated that the earth or structural metal frame of a building shall not be used as the sole equipment grounding conductor [Sections 250-51, 250-58 (a), 250-91 (c)] and that a grounded system conductor shall be run to each service [Sections 250-23, 250-27 (e) (f), 250-153 (d)].

The development of a low-resistance ground electrode is of paramount importance to satisfy these goals, primarily for system feeders from utilities, where the fault return path is via the ground, and secondarily as a backup to the equipment grounds, which may occasionally be open-circuited unintentionally. Logically, the lower the resistance of the grounding system, the more adequately these requirements are met. Yet, installations with lower available levels of ground-fault current do not require as low a value of grounding resistance as do larger systems with higher levels of ground-fault current. System ground resistances of less than 1 Ω may be obtained by the use of a number of individual electrodes connected together. Such a low resistance may only be required for large substations, transmission lines, or generating stations. Resistances in the 1–5 Ω range are generally found suitable for industrial plant substations and buildings and large commercial installations. Special grounding considerations for Arctic conditions will not be addressed, but additional information is available in References [20] and [10].

The 25 Ω value noted in the NEC [1] applies to the maximum resistance for a single made electrode. If a higher resistance is obtained for a single electrode, a second (paralleled) electrode is required. This should not be interpreted to mean that 25 Ω is a satisfactory level for a grounding system.

In contrast, the Canadian Electrical Code (CEC), CSA C22.1-1990 [2] uses a criterion of maximum station ground rise of 5000 volts (or less) under maximum ground fault conditions and step/touch voltages to be shown values stipulated in the CEC (basically these values are the same values given in IEEE Std 80-1986 [3]. Prior to 1978, the CEC used a criterion of station ground resistance required to be less than 1 Ω, which was found to be particularly burdensome for small capacity industrial type substations. The method stipulated in the CEC is based on sound rationale—the criterion is safety-based. However, its shortcomings are evident in the contractor-inspector interface where calculations are required rather than (relatively) simple ground resistance checks.

4.1.3 Resistivity of Soils

It is *strongly* recommended that the resistivity of the earth at the desired location of the connection be investigated. The resistivity of soils varies with the depth from the surface, the type and concentration of soluble chemicals in the soil, the moisture content, and the soil temperature. In other words, the resistivity is that of the electrolyte in the soil. The presence of surface water does not necessarily indicate low resistivity. Representative values of resistivity for general types of soils are given in Table 10 [14]. The effects of moisture and temperature are shown in Tables 11 [39] and 12 [4].

---

[16]The numbers in brackets correspond to those references listed in 4.5.

Table 10—Resistivity of Soils and Resistance of Single Rods

Soil Description	Group Symbol[*]	Average Resistivity (Ω·cm)	Resistance of 5/8 in (16 mm) x 10 ft (3 m) Rod (Ω)
Well graded gravel, gravel-sand mixtures, little or no fines	G W	60 000–100 000	180–300
Poorly graded gravels, gravel-sand mixtures, little or not fines	GP	100 000–250 000	300–750
Clayey gravel, poorly graded gravel, sand-clay mixtures	GC	20 000–40 000	60–120
Silty sands, poorly graded sand-silts mixtures	SM	10 000–50 000	30–150
Clayey sands, poorly graded sand-clay mixtures	SC	5000–20 000	15–60
Silty or clayey fine sands with slight plasticity	ML	3000–8000	9–24
Fine sandy or silty soils, elastic silts	MH	8000–30 000	24–90
Gravelly clays, sandy clays, silty clays, lean clays	CL	2500–6000[†]	17–18[†]
Inorganic Clays of high plasticity	CH	1000–5500[†]	3–16[†]

*The terminology used in these descriptions is from the United Soil Classification and is a standard method of describing soils in a geotechnical or geophysical report.
†These soils classification resistivity results are highly influenced by the presence of moisture.

Table 11—Effect of Moisture Content on Soil Resistivity

Moisture Content (% by weight)	Resistivity ($\Omega \cdot$ cm)		
	Top Soil	Sandy Loam	Red Clay
2	no data	185 000	no data
4	no data	60 000	no data
6	135 000	38 000	no data
8	90 000	28 000	no data
10	60 000	22 000	no data
12	35 000	17 000	180 000
14	25 000	14 000	55 000
16	20 000	12 000	20 000
18	15 000	10 000	14 000
20	12 000	9000	10 000
22	10 000	8000	9000
24	10 000	7000	8000

Table 12—Effect of Temperature on Soil Resistivity

Temperature (C°)	Resistivity (Ω · cm)
−5	70 000
0	30 000
0	10 000
10	8000
20	7000
30	6000
40	5000
50	4000

4.1.4 Calculation of Resistance to Earth

The resistance to earth may be calculated and measured. The calculation has been simplified to a great extent by the formulas developed in [16] and presented in Table 13. It should be stated that these formulas are approximations only and given the state of today's capabilities with respect to computer derived models of earth systems and grounding design, strong consideration to using those tools should be examined.

A simplified formula for the most widely-used electrode type, accurate to within 15% (resistance from a single 10 ft (3 m) long by 5/8 in (16 mm) diameter rod, in earth of uniform resistivity of ρ Ω · cm, is

$$R_g \ (rod) = \frac{p(\Omega \cdot cm)}{335 \ cm} \ \Omega \ . \tag{7}$$

Table 13—Formulas for the Calculation of Resistances to Ground

⊽	Hemisphere radius a	$R = \dfrac{\rho}{2\pi a}$
•	One ground rod length L, radius a	$R = \dfrac{\rho}{2\pi L}\left(\ln\dfrac{4L}{a} - 1\right)$
• •	Two ground rods $s > L$; spacing s	$R = \dfrac{\rho}{4\pi L}\left(\ln\dfrac{4L}{a} - 1\right) + \dfrac{\rho}{4\pi s}\left(1 - \dfrac{L^2}{3s^2} + \dfrac{2L^4}{5s^4}\cdots\right)$
••	Two ground rods $s < L$; spacing s	$R = \dfrac{\rho}{4\pi L}\left(\ln\dfrac{4L}{a} + \ln\dfrac{4L}{s} - 2 + \dfrac{s}{2L} - \dfrac{s^2}{16L^2} + \dfrac{s^4}{512L^4}\cdots\right)$
—	Buried horizontal wire length $2L$, depth $s/2$	$R = \dfrac{\rho}{4\pi L}\left(\ln\dfrac{4L}{a} + \ln\dfrac{4L}{s} - 2 + \dfrac{s}{2L} - \dfrac{s^2}{16L^2} + \dfrac{s^4}{512L^4}\cdots\right)$
L	Right-angle turn of wire length of arm L, depth $s/2$	$R = \dfrac{\rho}{4\pi L}\left(\ln\dfrac{2L}{a} + \ln\dfrac{2L}{s} - 0.2373 + 0.2146\dfrac{s}{L} + 0.1035\dfrac{s^2}{L^2} - 0.0424\dfrac{s^4}{L^4}\cdots\right)$
人	Three-point star length of arm L, depth $s/2$	$R = \dfrac{\rho}{6\pi L}\left(\ln\dfrac{2L}{a} + \ln\dfrac{2L}{s} + 1.071 - 0.209\dfrac{s}{L} + 0.238\dfrac{s^2}{L^2} - 0.054\dfrac{s^4}{L^4}\cdots\right)$
+	Four-point star length of arm L, depth $s/2$	$R = \dfrac{\rho}{8\pi L}\left(\ln\dfrac{2L}{a} + \ln\dfrac{2L}{s} + 2.912 - 1.071\dfrac{s}{L} + 0.645\dfrac{s^2}{L^2} - 0.145\dfrac{s^4}{L^4}\cdots\right)$
✳	Six-point star length of arm L, depth $s/2$	$R = \dfrac{\rho}{12\pi L}\left(\ln\dfrac{2L}{a} + \ln\dfrac{2L}{s} + 6.851 - 3.128\dfrac{s}{L} + 1.758\dfrac{s^2}{L^2} - 0.490\dfrac{s^4}{L^4}\cdots\right)$
✳	Eight-point star length of arm L, depth $s/2$	$R = \dfrac{\rho}{16\pi L}\left(\ln\dfrac{2L}{a} + \ln\dfrac{2L}{s} + 10.98 - 5.51\dfrac{s}{L} + 3.26\dfrac{s^2}{L^2} - 1.17\dfrac{s^4}{L^4}\cdots\right)$
○	Ring of wire diameter of ring D, diameter of wire d, depth $s/2$	$R = \dfrac{\rho}{2\pi^2 D}\left(\ln\dfrac{8D}{d} + \ln\dfrac{4D}{s}\right)$
—	Buried horizontal strip length $2L$, section a by b, depth $s/2$, $b < a/8$	$R = \dfrac{\rho}{4\pi L}\left(\ln\dfrac{4L}{a} + \dfrac{a^2 - \pi ab}{2(a+b)^2} + \ln\dfrac{4L}{s} - 1 + \dfrac{s}{2L} - \dfrac{s^2}{16L^2} + \dfrac{s^4}{512L^4}\cdots\right)$
⬨	Buried horizontal round plate radius a, depth $s/2$	$R = \dfrac{\rho}{8a} + \dfrac{\rho}{4\pi s}\left(1 - \dfrac{7}{12}\dfrac{a^2}{s^2} + \dfrac{33}{40}\dfrac{a^4}{s^4}\cdots\right)$
	Buried vertical round plate radius a, depth $s/2$	$R = \dfrac{\rho}{8a} + \dfrac{\rho}{4\pi s}\left(1 + \dfrac{7}{24}\dfrac{a^2}{s^2} + \dfrac{99}{320}\dfrac{a^4}{s^4}\cdots\right)$

*See Reference [16].

†Approximate formulas, including effects of images. Dimensions must be in centimeters to give resistance in ohms.

ρ = resistivity of earth in ohm–centimeters.

For 10 ft (3 m) rods of 1/2, 5/8, and 3/4 in (12.7, 15.88, and 19.05 mm) diameters, the grounding resistance may be quickly determined by dividing the soil resistivity ρ, Ω-cm, by 288, 298, and 307, respectively.

Multiple electrodes in parallel yield lower resistance to ground than a single electrode. Multiple rods are commonly used to provide the low grounding resistance required by high-capacity installations. Adding a second rod does not, however, provide a total resistance of half that of a single rod, unless the two are several rod lengths apart. A useful rule is that grounding systems of 2–24 rods placed one rod length apart in a line, hollow triangle, circle, or square will provide a grounding resistance divided by the number of rods and multiplied by the factor F taken from Table 14. Additional considerations with respect to step and touch potentials would be addressed by the geometry.

Table 14—Multiplying Factors for Multiple Rods

Number of Rods	F
2	1.16
3	1.29
4	1.36
8	1.68
12	1.80
16	1.92
20	2.00
24	2.16

Placing additional rods within the periphery of a square, circle, or other shape will not appreciably reduce the grounding resistance below that of the peripheral rods alone.

4.1.5 Current-Loading Capacity

One factor which should not be overlooked in designing a grounding system is the current-loading capacity of a connection to earth. The temperature and moisture conditions immediately surrounding the electrode have a direct effect on the resistivity of this section of the grounding circuit. Currents passing from the electrode into the earth will have a definite effect on these two conditions. Therefore, the current-loading capacity of a connection must be analyzed from the standpoint of the nature of the grounding circuit and the types of loading which it can normally be expected to carry. Information useful in this regard for steel rods in concrete (reinforcing bars) is given in [3], [17], [42], and [15], pp. 102–108.

Currents of low magnitude, even if of long duration, will result in relatively little heating. The effect of heat conduction and the movement of moisture due to capillary action will maintain, in most cases, the resistivity of the earth at the electrode close to the original value.

Where the earth must dissipate high currents for short durations, no appreciable amount of heat can be dissipated by the normal process of thermal conductivity. The permissible current density for a given temperature rise is inversely proportional to the square root of the soil resistivity. The effective resistance of the earth connection therefore depends on the number of such situations that could occur in succession before stable conditions in the earth are reestablished.

Since approximately 25% of the grounding resistance of each rod electrode occurs within a 0.1 ft (0.03 m) radius of the rod surface, serious heating and vaporization of the moisture adjacent to the rods may occur on heavy faults. When the moisture is boiled away, the effectiveness of the rod in the dried-out earth is substantially reduced, and arcing below the ground surface is likely. The boiling away of soil water results in steaming, or "smoking," at the ground surface near the electrode. To prevent the "smoking" electrodes, a maximum current per foot of rod length for the total rod system should not exceed the values as determined by the following formula:

$$I = \frac{34\ 800 \cdot d \cdot L}{\sqrt{p \cdot t}} \tag{8}$$

For a 1 ft, 5/8 in (0.32 m) rod, this yields 116 A in 2500 $\Omega \cdot$ cm soil and 58 A for 10 000 $\Omega \cdot$ cm soil

where

d	= rod diameter
L	= length in meters

ρ = ohm meter

t = seconds (valid for short time only)

Ground currents of high magnitude and long duration are unusual, but could occur as the result of ground faults that are not cleared promptly. If ground currents of this type are anticipated, the system must cover a relatively large area and employ a sufficient number of electrodes to keep the current density in the earth to a low value [3], [36].

4.1.6 Soil Treatment

Soil resistivity may be reduced anywhere from 15 to 90% by chemical treatment, (depending on the kind and texture of the soil) [23]. There are a number of chemicals suitable for this purpose, including sodium chloride, magnesium sulfate, copper sulfate, and calcium chloride. Common salt and magnesium sulfate are most commonly used.

Chemicals are generally applied by placing them in a circular trench around the electrode in such a manner as to prevent direct contact with the electrode. While the effects of treatment will not become apparent for a considerable period, they may be accelerated by saturating the area with water. This may be done by providing a trickle of water from piping at the electrode locations. Also, such treatment is not permanent and must be renewed periodically, depending on the nature of the chemical treatment and the characteristics of the soil. Chemical treatment also has adverse effects on the corrosion protection of the ground electrodes, which must be assessed ([13], [22], [411).

Soil chemical treatment is an active solution to the problem of high resistivity soils. To be effective, a regular maintenance scheme must be established to ensure low resistance grounding is achieved.

4.2 Ground Electrodes

Basically all ground electrodes may be divided into two groups. The first group comprises underground metallic piping systems, metal building frameworks, well casings, steel piling, and other underground metal structures installed for purposes other than grounding. The second group comprises electrodes specifically designed for grounding purposes.

Made electrodes may be subdivided into driven electrodes, steel reinforcing bars in below-ground concrete, buried strips or cables, grids, buried plates, and counterpoises. The type selected will depend on the type of soil encountered and the available depth. Grids are frequently used for substations or generating stations to provide equipotential areas throughout the entire station in locations where hazards to life and property would justify the higher cost. They also require the least amount of buried material for a given electrode resistance. Buried plates have not been used extensively in recent years because of the high cost as compared to rods or strips. Also, when used in small numbers they are the least efficient type of made electrode. The counterpoise is a form of buried cable electrode most often used to ground transmission-line towers and structures (see Tables 13 and 14 and Reference [39]).

When multiple electrodes are used, spacings of less than 10 ft (3 m) may not provide the most economical use of materials.

In selecting the number and size of grounding terminals, their current-discharge limitations must be recognized. If these are exceeded, the earth around the electrode may be exploded by steam generation or may be dried out to the extent of becoming nonconductive.

4.2.1 Existing Electrodes

Metal building frames are normally attached by long anchor bolts to their concrete foundations footings. The anchor bolts in concrete serve as electrodes, while the metal building frame is simply a grounding conductor. For safety grounding and for small distribution systems where the ground currents are of relatively low magnitude, such electrodes are usually preferred because they are economical in first cost. However, before reliance can be placed on any electrodes of this group, it is essential that their resistance to earth be measured to ensure that some unforeseen discontinuity has not seriously affected their suitability. Also, care should be exercised to ensure that all parts that might become disconnected are effectively bonded together.

4.2.2 Driven Electrodes

Driven electrodes are normally rods. Where soil conditions permit, a few deep rods are usually more satisfactory than a multiplicity of short rods, since the soil resistivity generally decreases (although this is not always the case [38]) with depth due to the increased moisture content. A number of design charts for the determination of optimum ground-rod dimensions and spacing for a given installation are given in [3] and [4], while other definitive work on driven rods is found in [11] and [12].

4.2.3 Concrete Encased Electrodes

Concrete below ground level is a semiconducting medium of about 3000 Ω cm resistivity at 20 °C, or somewhat lower than the average loam soil. Consequently, in earth of average or high resistivity, the encasement of rod or wire electrodes in concrete results in lower resistance than when a similar electrode is placed directly into earth. This is due to a reduction of the resistance of the material closest to the primary electrode, in much the same manner as chemical treatment of the earth reacts near the electrode. While it is justifiable to excavate or drill holes for the placement of concrete for ground grid purposes in some locations, the widespread use of steel reinforcing bars in concrete foundation and footings provides a ready-made supply of grounding electrodes. At structures utilizing this type of construction, it is only necessary to bring out an adequate electrical connection from a main reinforcing bar of each such footing for attachment to the building ground bus or structural steel [34].

Foundations may be of two types: continuous footings around the building periphery or spread column footings, which are vertical members tied at the top (above ground) by the walls. For the former type of foundation, one can tie the vertical rebar in the walls to the horizontal rebar in the footings to provide a continuous loop around the building. At each consecutive, or alternatively, at every second consecutive column location, the vertical rebar can be tapped with a similar material (rebar extension or similar) and affixed to the column. In this way, use of existing structural rebar can provide a superior earth (compared to burial outside of footing).

The other type of foundation, the column footing or spread footing, can be used similarly but without the benefits of the lower perimeter ground wire. In its place, an upper perimeter ground conductor should be installed (within the wall at or below grade). This ground conductor can be either rebar or copper ground conductor.

Each such footing electrode has a resistance equal to or lower than that of a driven rod of equal depth. The large number of such footing inherent to buildings will provide a net ground resistance considerably lower than that normally provided by other made electrode methods, generally below 1 Ω and frequently of the order of 0.25 Ω

Two methods may be used to connect the vertical rebar to the building columns. The first method ties the vertical rebar element to the anchor bolts. Thus, the steel columns are grounded through the bolts and nuts. The other method requires a pigtail of copper penetrating the top of the wall, this then being welded or bolted to the steel member.

Caution must be exercised in both the choosing of the size of the rebar for the available fault current and in the method in which the connections are made between rebar elements. Owing principally to the fact that this technique is not used widely and to the requirement for good connections for superior performance, this method may not be satisfactory for all building projects. In these projects, use of copper conductor instead of rebar elements is recommended.

Only footings at the building periphery are effective. For practical purposes the net grounding resistance (to remote earth) will not be lowered by "rebar ground rods," within the area encompassed by the periphery of the building. However, it should be noted as a precaution that lack of bonding between the anchor bolts and rebar may be responsible for:

- occasional failure to tower footing structure from current passage through the intervening concrete under heavy fault conditions, and

- dry-out weakening of intervening concrete from moderate continuous current flow through the concrete where the building process involved continuous current leakage as in chemical cell (dc) plants.

To ensure that high magnitude ground fault currents do not destructively explode the concrete due to rapid drying out of the moisture in the concrete surrounding the rebar, the size of the rebars chosen for this duty is critical. The current per foot or rebar is summarized in Table 15.

Table 15—Current Capacity of Building Rebar

Rod Diameter		Amperes/Foot	
Inches	Bar #	5 cycle clearing time	1 second clearing time
1/2	4	112	32
5/8	5	135	39
3/4	6	157	46
1	8	200	58
1 3/8	11	270	78

Test results and design data for the determination of the ground resistance of single and multiple concrete-encased footing electrodes are given in [17].

Steel rods in concrete in (irregular) excavations in rock or very rocky soil have been found greatly superior to other types of made electrodes. This electrode type provides additional grounding for the majority of the steel towers of high-voltage transmission lines.

4.2.4 Other Electrodes

Where bedrock is near the surface, or where sand is encountered, the soil is apt to be very dry and of high resistivity, and it is necessary to have an extensive earthing connection. Under such conditions, buried metal strips, wires, or cables offer the most economical solution. Since the effectiveness of this type of electrode of lightning discharges is a function of its inductance, the use of a number of well-spaced shorter strips in parallel is preferable to one or more long strips. The depth at which the strips are buried may not be critical. However, as Table 12 indicates, temperature (and thus depth) can have an effect in areas where soil temperatures can go below freezing. Tests by the National Bureau of Standards [32] show that the resistance decreases only about 5%, when the burial depth is increased from 18 in to 36 in (0.5 m to 1 m), based on uniform soil resistivity. Similarly, the effect of conductor size is extremely small.

The preferred practice with plate electrodes is to bury them on edge, because a minimum of excavation is required and it is possible to obtain better contact with the soil when backfilling. There appears to be little difference between the effective resistance of horizontal and vertical plates. For commonly used plates of 10–20 ft^2 (0.9–1.9 m^2), the optimum burial depth is 5–8 ft (1.52–2.4 m).

4.2.5 Substation Grounding

At large electrical substations, the ground-fault current is generally high, and the likelihood of persons present there could also be high. Problems from this are high shock hazard from touching grounded metal parts while standing on the earth, walking on earth within the substation, or while walking outside the substation in contact with the fence. IEEE Std 80-1986 (ANSI) [3] amply describes this problem and provides design data for such grounding systems. The basic characteristics and design elements for extensive grid systems are given in [21], and numerous references concerning this subject exist in IEEE Std 80-1986 (ANSI) [3].

Coarse crushed rock (example: granite), is normally spread all over the surface of the soil within such a substation grid area, not for housekeeping reasons, but to provide a high-resistance surface treatment to reduce the hazard from step potential to persons within this area during a severe fault. Granite rock (granite porphyry), even when wet from rain, has a high insulation resistance. ($4.5 \cdot 10^5$ Ω·cm wet, $1.3 \cdot 10^8$ Ω·cm dry [3]). It is not unreasonable to be unable to use good quality crushed stone due to the location the substation may be in, so other means to increase the safety of personnel may be required. Asphalt can be used because of its high wet resistivity (>1 000 000 Ω·cm).

4.2.6 Transferred Earth Potentials

"Transferred earth potentials refers to the phenomenon of the earth potential of one location (or voltages referred to that earth potential) appearing at another location where there is a contrasting earth potential" [31].

The ground potential rise of a substation may be on the order of some 5000 V, which may be transferred out to a nonfault location by a ground conductor (or metal pipe, rail, etc.) leaving the station. This situation is to be avoided to ensure both personnel and equipment protection at the nonfaulted end.

Steps to alleviate this transferred potential problem include the bonding together of ground mats (that are within a range of approximately 100–300 ft apart), and the use of isolation transformers. This problem was recognized by utilities in the application of pilot wire protection where the low voltage conductors (pilot wire circuit) were interconnecting two remote ground grids. Most of the ameliorating techniques were based on the utilities solution to this basic problem.

Rail and Pipe Isolation joints may be used to limit the travel of Transferred potentials. Additional information on this subject is found in References [5], [6], [7], [31], and [33].

4.3 Methods and Techniques of Construction

4.3.1 Choice of Rods

Ground rods are manufactured in diameters of 3/8, 1/2, 5/8, 3/4, and 1 in (9.53, 12.7, 15.88, 19.05, and 25.4 mm) and in lengths of 5–40 ft (1.5–12.2 m). For most applications, the diameters of 1/2, 5/8, and 3/4 in (12.7, 15.88, and 19.05 mm) are satisfactory. The NEC [1] specified that rods of steel or iron shall be at least 5/8 in (15.88 mm) in diameter and that rods of nonferrous materials shall not be less than 1/2 in (12.7 mm) in diameter. Copper-clad steel, one of the most common types of rods, permits driving to considerable depth without destruction of the rod itself, while the copper coat permits direct copper-to-copper connection between the ground wire and the rod. In addition to the copper-clad steel, galvanized steel rods and stainless steel rods are available. Stainless rods must be reviewed with soil conditions to ensure against the possibility of stress corrosion cracking [19].

Some rods are available in sections for ease of driving. As each section is driven toward ground level, another section is added by use of a coupling (threaded, compression sleeve, or welded), making a continuous conductor. A removable stud or special driving head will take the driving blows and avoid damage to the threads at the end of the rod. For safety reasons, rods should be driven so that no unguarded length remains above ground.

The effect of the rod diameter on the resistance of the connection to earth is small. The mechanical rigidity required for driving mainly determines the diameter of the rod. It is advantageous to select the smallest diameter rod that meets the driving requirements. Average soil conditions will permit the use of the 1/2 in (12.7 mm) rod. The 5/8 in (15.88 mm) rod can be driven in nearly all types of soil, and the 3/4 in (19.05 mm) rod may be reserved for exceptionally hard driving conditions or for deep-driven rods.

For ordinary soil condition, the 10 ft (3 m) length of rod has become fairly well established as a minimum standard length to meet the code requirement of a minimum of 8 buried feet (2.44 buried meters).

4.3.2 Methods of Driving Rods

Sledging requires a minimum of driving equipment, but may require considerable time per foot of rod. A modification of the sledging process, consisting of a chuck and sliding hammer, permits the work to be carried on at a level convenient to the worker without a ladder or auxiliary platform. An additional advantage is that the blow is delivered to the rod at a point not far from the ground line, thus permitting rods to be driven to greater depths than would be possible by hand sledging. If rods are to be driven on a comparatively large scale, it is desirable to provide power driving equipment. Electric, pneumatic, and gasoline-driven hammers are available, the first two requiring sources of power. Regardless of the type of driving tool used, precautions should be taken to prevent mushrooming of the head.

4.3.3 Connecting to Electrodes

Connections to electrodes are usually made by one of several means. The first of these methods involves the use of mechanical fittings, which are readily available, simple to install, and disconnectable for measurements of resistance to earth; and they have a long history of satisfactory usage. Although corrosion has sometimes presented a problem, treatment of the joint as an ordinary electrical connection in a corrosive environment eliminates most of the problems in this respect. Mechanical connections should, if at all possible, be accessible for inspection and servicing.

The second method, an exothermic or weld-type process of connecting to the electrode, has increased in usage in recent years because of the savings in time and costs when many connections must be made. This method provides a permanent connection, eliminates contact resistance, is relatively corrosion free. It also permits the use of smaller copper cable (when connected with exothermic versus mechanical fittings) because of the 1083 °C maximum temperature limitation, as compared to the maximum of 250 °C–350 °C usually permitted for some mechanical connections [3]. (The NEC article 250-94 imposes a minimum conductor size limitation, however.) This method does, however, have certain inherent limitations. It requires separate disconnecting means, such as above-ground bolted joints, for measurements of resistance to earth. It also requires a certain amount of training, and it cannot be used in the presence of volatile or explosive mixtures, or where the gaseous products of the operation would interfere with nearby operations. Connections in inclement weather can also be difficult if sufficient protection is not provided.

The third widely accepted method, compression connections, are easy to install, provide low contact resistance and minimizes possibility of poor connections. These connectors, however, cannot be disconnected for measurements of resistance to earth. Other methods of jointing, such as brazing, are satisfactory if properly done.

IEEE Std 837-1989 (ANSI) [8] provides a means of qualifying connectors used in grounding. Many of the three types of connectors discussed (mechanical, exothermic, and compression) meet the IEEE Std 837-1989 (ANSI) [8] requirements.

4.3.4 Joining to Underground Piping Systems

Joining to pipe presents several problems. Clamp-type fittings are relatively expensive, since they must obviously accommodate a large pipe in addition to the relatively small conductor. Welding or brazing to the pipe will cause localized stress, which may impair the function of the pipe, particularly if it contains fluid under high pressure. Where connection is deemed necessary the welding is technically acceptable and preferable if local piping codes allow. If the grounds are affixed before stress relief is applied (and is scheduled), this should offset any local stresses made by the grounding connection. An additional difficulty may be the onset of corrosion if electrochemical conditions are right (see 4.4.5).

4.3.5 Joining to Structural Steel

Bolted fittings lend themselves best to structural steel that can be field drilled but not welded. These are available in a number of shapes and sizes to accommodate the range of conductors. Material for the clamps or protective finishes applied to the clamps should be chosen so as to be satisfactory for both the grounding wire and the steel or iron from the corrosion standpoint. Brazing and the exothermic process are also used when connecting to structural steel, but should be restricted to application that will not affect the structural properties of the steel.

4.3.6 Preparing the Joint

It is important that the surface of any connection be cleaned of any insulating medium, such as insulation, grease, paint, dirt, or corrosion before making the connection.

4.4 Measurement of Resistance to Earth

4.4.1 Need for Measurement

Many indeterminate factors exists in any formula for the calculation of the resistance to earth. Total reliance should not be placed on the calculated results. For example, the soil resistivity varies inversely with the soil temperature and directly with the moisture content and may vary with the depth. The only certain way to determine the resistance is to measure it after the system has been completed. A desirable refinement is to measure the resistance of each electrode during installation.

4.4.2 Methods for Measuring

The principles used in the measurement of resistance to earth are essentially the same as those used for measuring other types of electrical resistances. The various methods available all make use of two auxiliary electrodes in addition to the one under test and may be placed in the following three general classes:

1) The three-point method, in which the resistance to earth of the electrode under test and of the auxiliary electrodes is measured two electrodes at a time, in series. This method is suitable for measuring the resistance to earth of isolated ground electrodes or small grounding installations. It is not suitable for the measurement of low-resistance installations.

2) The fall-of-potential method, which involves passing a known alternating current through the electrode under test and one of the auxiliary electrodes and measuring the potential drop between these electrodes and a secondary auxiliary electrode set at various distances between the two fixed electrodes. This method may be subject to considerable error if stray ground currents (at the same frequency of the Test Meter) are present, or if pipes or other conductors are buried near the test electrode.

3) The ratio method, which involves measurements of the ratio of the resistance to earth of an auxiliary test electrode to the series resistance to earth of the electrode under test and a second auxiliary electrode. Multiplying this ratio by the series resistance gives the effective resistance of the ground electrodes. This method is more satisfactory than the triangulation methods since ratios of the resistance of the auxiliary test electrode to the resistance of the electrode under test may be as high as 300:1.

A more complete treatment of these three methods may be found in References [4] and [18].

Commercially available portable testing instruments provide the most convenient and satisfactory means for measuring insulation resistance are not suitable, however, because they cannot measure sufficiently low-resistance values. Also, ordinary low-resistance ohm meters lack sufficient voltage of separating out the grounding resistance of the auxiliary electrodes needed to make the test.

Precision in measurements of the resistance to earth is difficult to obtain and is usually not required. Normally, an accuracy on the order of 25% is sufficient in view of the many variables.

It is desirable, in measuring the resistance of the completed system, to allow some time to elapse before measurements are made, so that the earth around the electrodes will be consolidated. This does not apply to the auxiliary electrodes required in the test, since their resistance is negated in the test period.

4.4.3 Periodic Testing

Tests should be made periodically after the original installation and test so that it can be determined whether the resistance is remaining constant or is increasing. If later tests show that the resistance is increasing to an undesirable value, steps should be taken to reduce the resistance either by remaking corroded connections, by adding electrodes, by increasing the moisture content, or by chemical treatment.

4.4.4 Earth Resistivity Measurements

The commercial portable instruments available for measuring the grounding electrode resistance normally may be used to measure the soil resistivity as well. For this purpose they are connected to four short electrodes spaced uniformly in a line. Spacing between the two center electrodes is a direct measure of the effective depth desired for the resistivity, that is, for example, a 10 ft (3 m) spacing will yield the average resistivity of the top 10 ft (3 m) of soil, and so on. This test method is known as the 4 pin Wenner Method and is among the most popular methods of determining earth resistivity.

The instrument yields an ohmic reading, which when, multiplied by two times the spacing in centimeters and multiplied by π, is the soil resistivity in $\Omega \cdot cm$. Full instructions for this test are provided with each test instrument. Other methods are fully described in References [4].

4.4.5 Electrical Grounding and Corrosion

The basic objectives of a sound electrical grounding system are safety of personnel, reliability of equipment operation, fault current return and to limit transient over voltages. After these objectives have been satisfied, the effect of the grounding installation on corrosion must be considered. Systems, equipment and lighting sometimes unknowingly contribute to the corrosion of underground conductors, structures, and piping. (See [25], p. 25; [26–28]; [30]; and [35].)

The problem is galvanic corrosion. This type of corrosion is caused by electrically connected dissimilar metals which form a galvanic cell. Under these conditions the following five factors determine the rate of corrosion:

a) The potential difference the two metals.
b) The ratio of the exposed areas of the two metals.
c) The resistance of the electrolyte.
d) The resistance of the external circuit.
e) Stray currents between electrodes, conductors, structures, and pipes.

Copper, the metal usually used for grounding, is a noble metal and can have serious corrosive effects on underground structures made of iron or steel which are electrically connected to the copper. These structures include underground pipe lines, conduits, building steel, buried tanks and buried lead-sheathed cables. Figure 62 shows the galvanic cell that results when steel and copper are electrically connected together. The steel may be a pipeline or conduit, the copper a ground rod, and the external connection could be conduit, the copper a ground rod, and the external connection could be through pipe-rack steel or through a ground rod connected directly to the conduit. The relative positions of steel (iron) and copper in the electromotive series, Table 16, produces a potential of 0.38 V, and according to Ohm's law, a current flows, with the soil (the electrolyte), completing the circuit. It is where the current leaves the steel (anode) and enters the soil that we have our trouble, namely, corrosion.

A dc current of 1 A flowing for one year will corrode away 20 lbs of steel, 22 lbs of copper, 75 lbs of lead, or 26 lbs of zinc. Thus, we see that the amount of current associated with corrosion. With greater current, more metal will corrode away.

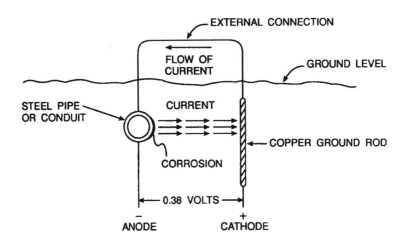

Figure 62—Galvanic Cell-Dissimilar Metals

Table 16—Electromotive Series of Metals

Metal	Potential	
Barium	2.90	Base End or Anodic End
Calcium	2.87	
Sodium	2.71	
Magnesium	2.40	
Aluminum	1.70	
Zinc	0.76	
Nickel	0.23	
Lead	0.12	
Iron	0.04	
Hydrogen	0.00	
Bismuth	-0.23	
Copper	-0.34	
Silver	-0.80	
Mercury	-0.80	
Gold	1.50	Noble End or Cathodic End

The potential difference between two metals will influence the amount of current that will flow between them. The greater the potential, the greater the current and therefore the greater the rate of corrosion.

The resistance of the earth (electrolyte) will limit the current flow.

While total current is dependent on the potential difference between the two metals and the resistance between them, the intensity of the anode current is a function of the ratio of the area, the current intensity is small. This is one of basic principles in corrosion engineering and is used as a control factor in design.

A small anode and a large cathode should not be installed. In this case, the total current is confined in a small space and the current density is large. An example if this would be an underground pipeline running up and onto a ground pipe rack. The resulting copper-steel couple is made worse when the pipe is coated, as no coating is 100% effective. Small pinholes may appear in the coating, exposing the steel. The current is then concentrated at these pinholes, causing leaks to occur in a very short time.

The electromotive series does not present all the facts about corrosion; it presents only its initial tendencies. The actual rate of corrosion is determined by the current, but the electromotive series determines which metals will waste away and which ones will remain unchanged.

The metals with positive values in Table 16 are on the base or anodic end of the series; these metals will corrode. The metals with the negative values are on the noble or cathodic end; these metals will protected. Thus the name "Cathodic Protection."

When a metal is the cathode, it is protected and will not corrode.

The resistance of the electrolyte, or soil, is one of the most important factors that affects the flow of current associated with galvanic corrosion. By Ohm's law, we find that the lower the resistance of the electrolyte, the larger the corrosion current. Consequently, the lower the soil resistivity, the greater the galvanic corrosion.

By using a different metal than copper for grounding, the copper-steel galvanic couple can be eliminated. If this metal were closer to iron in the electromotive series, there would be a smaller potential, therefore the galvanic couple would be less. The metal should have good electrical conductivity, which a ground must have, because a ground must be offer low impedance to fault current and lighting. It should be noted that steel rebar (and the like), when encased in concrete, have approximately the same potential as copper and thus will not corrode.

Steel (carbon and stainless) has been used, and zinc has been recommended, for ground rods. Steel requires cathodic protection, as the steel rod may rust unless the more expensive stainless rods (see 4.3.1) are used.

Galvanized steel rods would not be used in actual grounding because the zinc will corrode away and expose bare steel, which would rust. Instead we would use a zinc anode, which consists of a small steel core embedded in zinc. These come in many sizes, but the sizes that are best suited for a ground rod are designated by the American Zinc Institute as AZI-2-30 and AZI-4-60. The first number is the cross-sectional area in square inches, and the second number is the weight in pounds. Each is 5 ft (1.52 m) long.

Metal pairs, oxides, and electrolytic films can also be viewed as basic rectifying junctions that lead to electrolysis and metal migration in ac systems if stray or capacitive currents are present.

Cathodic protection means include also consumable anodes, e.g., Zinc, Magnesium, and low-voltage rectifiers or drainage panels that bias the protected metal [25]. Active protection in the form of a dc impressed current system can also be installed to protect any susceptible metals in the ground from corrosion effects.

The corrosion problem is of considerable importance in dc systems, such as mining or transit systems. with negative running rails, where stray current and grounding control is practiced and accessible mitigation bonds to structures may be provided [37].

4.5 References

[1] ANSI/NFPA 70-1990, National Electrical Code[17]

[2] CSA C22.1-1990, Canadian Electrical Code[18]

[3] IEEE Std 80-1986, Guide for Safety in AC Substation Grounding (ANSI).[19]

[4] IEEE Std 81-1983, IEEE Guide for Measuring Earth Resistivity, Ground Impedance and Earth Surface Potentials of a Ground System in Part I: Normal Measurements.

[5] IEEE Std 242- 1986, Recommended Practice for Protection and Coordination of Industrial and Commercial Power Systems (ANSI) (IEEE Buff Book).

[6] IEEE Std 367-1987, Recommended Practice for Determining Electric Power Station Ground Potential Rise and Induced Voltage From a Power Fault (ANSI).

[7] IEEE Std 487-1980, Guide for Protection of Wire-Line Communication Facilities Serving Electric Power Stations (ANSI).

[8] IEEE Std 837-1989, Standard for Qualifying Permanent Connections used in Substation Grounding (ANSI).

[9] Bashiki, R. S., Osterberg, C. K, and Dawalibi, F. "Earth Resistivity Measurements Using Cylindrical Electrodes at Short Spacings," IEEE *PWRD*-2, no. 1, Jan. 1987, p. 64.

[10] Beck, R. T., and Yu, L. "Design Considerations for Arctic Grounding Systems," *IEEE 1987 P CIC Conference Record*.

[11] Blattner, C. J. "Analysis of Soil Resistivity Test Methods in Two Layer Earth," *IEEE PAS-104*, no. 12, Dec. 1985.

[12] Blattner, C. J. "Prediction of Soil Resistivity and Ground Rod Resistance for Deep Ground Electrodes," *IEEE PAS-99*, no. 5, Sept./Oct. 1980.

[13] Coleman, W. E., and Frostick, H. "Electrical Grounding and Cathodic Protection at the Fairless Works," presented by the AIEE Subcommittee on Cathodic Protection at the 1954 AIEE Winter General Meeting.

[14] Cully, R. W., Jacoditis, F. L., and Middleton, R. S. "E-phase System for Detection of Buried Granular Deposits, Symposium on Modern Innovations in Subsurface Explorations," 54th Annual Meeting of Transportation Research Boards.

[15] Dick, W. K., and Holliday, H. R. "Impulse and Alternating Current Tests on Grounding Electrodes in Soil Environment," *IEEE PAS-97*, no 1, Jan./Feb. 1978.

[16] Dwight, H. B. "Calculation of Resistance to Ground. AIEE Transactions," vol. 55, Dec. 1936, pp. 1319–1328.

[17] Fagan, E. J., and Lee, R. H. "The Use of Concrete Enclosed Reinforcing Rods as Grounding Electrodes," *IEEE Transactions on Industry and General Applications*, vol IGA-6, July/Aug 1970, pp. 337–348.

---

[17]NFPA publications are available from Publications Sales, National Fire Protection Association, 1 Batterymarch Park, P.O. Box 9101, Quincy, MA 02269-9101, USA.
[18]CSA publications are available from the Canadian Standards Association (Standards Sales), 178 Rexdale Blvd., Rexdale, Ontario, Canada M9W 193.
[19]IEEE publications are available from the Institute of Electrical and Electronics Engineers, Service Center, 445 Hoes Lane, P.O. Box 1331, Piscataway, NJ 08855-1331, USA.

[18] Fink, D. G., and Carroll, J. M. Eds. *Standard Handbook for Electrical Engineers*. New York: McGraw-Hill Book Company, 1968.

[19] Fowler, N. L., and Lewicki, T. F. Proposal to NEC Code Committee for Section 250-83 (c) (2), "Revise this Paragraph to Delete Stainless Steel," 22 Oct. 1990.

[20] Gill, H. W. "Design Problems for an Electric Power System in an Arctic Region," *IEEE Transactions on Industry Applications*, vol. IA-10, No. 2, Mar./Apr. 1974.

[21] Gross, E. T. B., Chitnis, B. V., and Stratton, L. J. "Grounding Grids for High-voltage Stations," *AIEE Transactions on Power Apparatus and Systems*, vol 72, Aug. 1953, pp. 799—810.

[22] Headlee, J. F. "Cathodic Protection for Steel Mill Grounding Systems," *Iron and Steel Engineer*, Mar. 1954.

[23] Jones, W. R. "Bentonite Rods Assure Ground Rod Installation in Problem Soils," *IEEE PES Transactions*, vol. PAS-99, no. 4, July/Aug. 1980.

[24] Kinyon, A. L. "Earth Resistivity Measurements for Grounding Grids," *AIEE Transactions*, vol. 20, Dec. 1961, pp. 795–800.

[25] Lawson, V. L. "Problems and Detection of Line Anchor and Substation Ground Grid Corrosion," *IEEE Transactions on Industry Applications*, vol. IA-24, no. 1, Jan./Feb. 1988.

[26] Manohar, V. N., and Nagar, R. P. "Design of Steel Earthing Grids in India," *IEEE PAS-98*, no. 6, Nov./Dec. 1979.

[27] Manual on Underground Corrosion Control in Rural Electric Systems, REA Bulletin 161-23, Sept. 1981.

[28] McIntosh, D. H. "Grounding Where Corrosion Protection is Required," *IEEE Transactions on Industry Applications*, vol. IA-18, no. 6, Nov./Dec. 1982.

[29] Meliopoulos, A. P., Papalexopoulos, A.D., Webb, R. P., and Blattner, C. J. "Estimation of Soil Parameters from Driven Rod Measurements," *IEEE PAS-103*, no. 9, Sept. 1984.

[30] Nelson, J.P., and Holm, W. K. "A Cathodically Protected Electrical Substation Ground Grid," *IEEE Transactions on Industry Applications*, vol. IA-21, no. 2, Mar. 1985, pp. 357.

[31] Nichols, N., and Shipp, David D., "Designing to Avoid hazardous Transferred Earth Potentials," *IEEE Transactions on Industry Applications*, vol. IA-18, no. 4, July/Aug. 1982.

[32] Peters, O. S. "Ground Connections for Electric Systems," *Technologic Papers of the Bureau of Standards*. Washington, DC: National Bureau of Standards, 1918.[20]

[33] Pilot Wire Insulation and Protection, IL 41-971.4, Westinghouse Electric Corporation-Relay Instrument Division.

[32] Preminger, J., "Evaluation of Concrete Encased Electrodes," *IEEE Transactions on Industry Applications*, vol. IA-11, no. 6, Nov./Dec. 1975.

[34] Rajan, S., and Venugopalan, S. I. "Corrosion and Grounding Systems," *IEEE Transactions on Industry Applications*, vol. IA-13, no. 4, July/Aug. 1977, pp. 297.

---

[20]This document may be obtained only by libraries. An interlibrary loan form must be sent to NIST, Interlibrary Loan Dept., Gaithersburg, MD 20899 USA.

[35] Rudenberg, R. "Grounding Principles and Practice-I: Fundamental Considerations on Ground Currents," *Electrical Engineering*, vol. 64, Jan. 1945, pp. 1–13.

[36] Shaffer, R. E., and Venugopalan, S. I. "Stray Current Control in Dade County Metrorail System," *IEEE IAS Annual Conference Record*, no. 80CH1575-0, 1980.

[37] Sunde, E. D. *Earth Conduction Effects in Transmission Systems*, Chapter 2. New York: Macmillan, 1968.

[38] Tagg, G. F. *Earth Resistances*. New York: Pitman, 1964.

[39] Telford, W. M., Geldart, L. P., Sheriff, R. E., and Keys, D. A. *Applied Geophysics*. Cambridge England: Cambridge University Press, 1976.

[40] Thapar, B., Ferrer, O., and Blank, D. A. "Ground Resistance of concrete Foundations in Substation Yards," *IEEE PWRD*, vol. 5, no. 1, Jan. 1990.

[41] Wiener, P. A. "Comparison of concrete Encased Grounding Electrodes to Driven Ground Rods," *1969 IEEE ICPS Conference Record*.

[42] Zaborsky, J., and Rittenhouse, J.W. "Design Charts for Determining Optimum Ground-Rod Dimensions," *AIEE Transactions on Power Apparatus and Systems*, vol. 72, Aug. 1953, pp. 810—817.

Chapter 5

Sensitive Electronic Equipment Grounding

5.1 Introduction

The grounding of sensitive electronic equipment, such as computers, programmable logic controllers, process plants, distributed control systems, and similar electronic equipment, has been found to be one of the important items in achieving useful operation from these systems. The term "computer(s)" will be used for both computers and other sensitive electronic equipment in this chapter. The same rules apply. The low operating voltage of computers and other sensitive electronic equipment makes then susceptible to random voltages far below levels that are perceptible to humans and that have no effect on electrical power equipment. For example, sensitive electronic equipment is highly sensitive to static voltage charges generated by humans in simple body movements. Certainly the voltages injected into the earth by lightning strokes even within several thousand feet, unless suitable neutralization is accomplished, can cause malfunction and can possibly damage the equipment.

Much has been learned—not in how to prevent these sources of interference, but how to prevent their entrance into sensitive electronic equipment systems. With the means now available, malfunctions and damage from ground-transferred voltages can be eliminated.

5.2 Definitions

computer: This will refer to, in a generic sense, all sensitive electronic equipment.

electrode: (See Chapter 4.)

It must be noted that contrary to popular notion, the National Electrical Code (NEC) [1] does not favor the use of ground rods. Section 250-81 [1][21] states that if the following items are available, they are to be used first and bonded together to form the grounding electrode system:

1) Metal underground water pipe
2) Metal frame of the building, where effectively grounded
3) Concrete-encased electrode
4) Ground ring

Section 250-83 states that if none of the above is available, then and only then can you use any of the following:

1) Other local metal underground systems or structures
2) Rod and pipe electrodes
3) Plate electrodes

One of the most effective ground electrode systems is a ground ring tied to the building steel at suitable intervals. Concrete Encased Electrodes connected to the building steel, making the building steel effectively grounded, is not only an effective ground electrode system, but cost efficient too [8].

neutral: The point where the potential is equal in amplitude from ever other conductor [4]. The term "neutral" also refers to the National Electrical Code's "Identified Conductor." There may be occasions where a single-phase two-wire power source; a three-phase delta connection with one side center tapped; or a corner delta grounded system is referred to or used. In this case, the term "neutral" will refer to the conductor that is intentionally connected to ground.

noisy ground: The opposite of a quiet ground. A noisy ground is an electrical connection to a ground point that produces or injects spurious voltages into the computer system through the connection to ground.

quiet ground: This term is used in many computer installations and instruction manuals, papers, and other such documents. IEEE Std 100-1988 (ANSI) [4] defines "quiet ground" in terms of health-care facilities. It is "A system of

---

[21]The numbers in brackets correspond to those of the references listed in 5.10.

grounding conductors, insulated from portions of the conventional grounding of the power system, which interconnects the grounds of electric appliances for the purpose of improving immunity to electromagnetic noise." When used with respect to computer systems, the term "quiet ground" is usually vague and undefined in computer manuals.

For our use, a point on a ground system which does not inject spurious voltages into the computer system will be termed a "quiet ground." There are no standards to measure how quiet a quiet ground is. This is really a system that does not inject such voltages, rather than a grounding electrode type, such as an isolated grounding electrode.

There is no real isolation between electrodes. The earth has resistance and therefore it should be considered as an electrical element (resistance, induction, or impedance) in an electrical circuit. There is always a current flowing in the earth, which produces voltage differences between electrodes, even a few feet apart. Not only are there differences, but these differences vary from second to second, particularly during electrical storms.

zero reference: This is usually inferred to be ground or earth. Unfortunately, the earth may not be at zero potential. This misconception probably comes from the days of radio, when vacuum-tube sets used the metallic chassis as a common electrical ground return point in the circuit. The ground symbol was used for one side of' each tube's filament circuit. In addition, some of the control grids may have used aground" symbol in the circuit. On a vacuum-tube chassis, the metallic surface can, for the high voltages used, serve as an equal-potential surface. Unfortunately, the earth ground is not an equal-potential surface and should not be thought of as a point of zero reference, but as a point in an electrical circuit that contains different potentials, depending on where on the surface of the earth the connection is made.

The earth is considered by some as an infinite electrical power sink, able to absorb any amount of electrical power. Again, the earth must be considered as part of an electrical circuit in cases where continuous current is concerned. Even with lightning and static, there is a circuit.

5.3 History of Computer Grounding

5.3.1 Satisfying Code Requirements

Because of the necessity for safety and the requirements of the NEC [1], computers were grounded. First they were grounded to the electrical power equipment grounding system of the building in which they were located. The equipment ground conductor was either a green insulated wire or a bare wire. In many cases, the metallic conduit served this purpose. The equipment ground was connected, at the building service, to the incoming neutral conductor from the utility. At this point the metallic enclosure was bonded, connected to the neutral, to the equipment grounding conductor, and to earth. Earth could be a driven rod, and/or a metallic cold-water pipe. The building steel, either intentionally or unintentionally, was also connected into the building grounding system.

There was no particular requirement as to what part of the power system ground the computer ground was to be connected, so the connections were generally made to the ground conductor at the plug, receptacle, or panel supplying power to the computer. This satisfied the NEC [1] requirements in that no one could be shocked by touching the computer enclosure under a phase-to-ground fault condition. As computer components became more complex and sensitive to lower voltages, it was found that transient voltages could be harmful and damaging to the solid state-devices.

Electrical transient voltages were traced to the multiple connections from the neutral conductor to the ground system. In a commercial building it is not unusual to find the neutral conductor connected to ground/earth at the transformer. At each electrical service to every building served by that transformer, the neutral would be connected to ground. It is not unusual to find the appliance and :receptacle panels' neutral bus bar connected to the metallic panel enclosure, which is an NEC [1] violation. One study showed 20% of the neutral conductors accidentally faulted to ground in circuits supplying lighting fixtures [10]. With multiple connections of the ground system, to which the computer was connected, the current flow transferred voltages into the grounding system of the computers, causing errors or worse. Fig 63 illustrates one of the conditions. The term "quiet ground" originated when isolated grounds were initiated, in about 1960. In comparison, the term "noisy ground" was applied to electrical power-system grounds, where multiple ground connections were made to them, as shown in Fig 64.

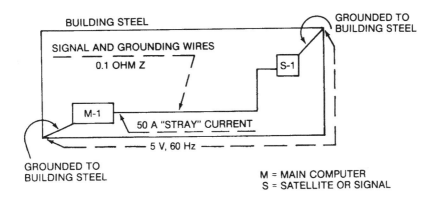

Figure 63—5 V Pickup from Multiple Grounding-Current Conducting Paths in Building Steel

5.3.2 Noise in Power System Ground

With the increasing complexity of computer systems, it became necessary to have satellite computers, or remote terminals, placed away from the location of the main computer. The remote computer locations had power supplies. These could be supplies from the main computer power system, but more likely they would be from another part of the building. It is not unusual for grounding (bonding) systems of a building to have measurable voltage differences from point to point, due to the current flow, either 60 Hz or transient high frequency. Thus, a connection to the power system ground at the remote location could connect the remote ground to something a few volts different in potential from the main computer ground. This then would inject the voltage difference between the two ground connections into the system, interfering with the normal computer signals.

With multiple ground paths and the neutral conductor connected, either intentionally or unintentionally, to the ground system at multiple points, the neutral return current could flow uncontrolled over the ground system. At each point where the neutral is connected to ground, and parallel paths exist, the current will divide according to the inverse impedance of the circuit per Ohm's Law. (See Fig 64.)

From this uncontrolled current flow over the grounding system, the power system became known as a "dirty," or noisy, ground. The computer personnel resolved to have nothing further to do with such building grounding systems.

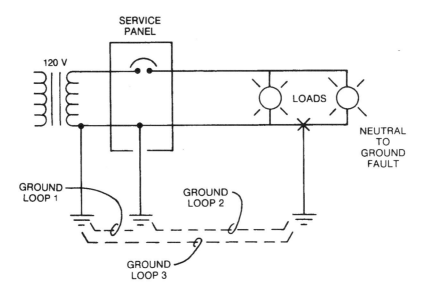

Figure 64—Multiple Neutral-Ground Current Paths

5.4 System or Equipment to Be Grounded

5.4.1 Power System

With electrical power systems, there are at least two groups or classes of grounding:

1) *System Grounding.* The grounding of some part of the electrical power supply system, usually the system neutral.
2) *Equipment Grounding.* The grounding of all the metallic equipment and enclosure frames, through bonding of all component parts and their connection to ground.

5.4.2 Sensitive Electronic Equipment (Computers)

Like the electrical power supply system, computers have diversified systems to be grounded:

1) *Signal Common Grounding.* The signal common is also referred to as the "DC Signal Common." The zero reference system for data lines, and the signal portion in general, represents the sensitive neutral of the computer. This is one of the systems that is sensitive to transient voltages and requires a stable reference point, with respect to a voltage potential.
2) *DC Power Supply Reference Ground Bus.* The computer may have several different dc voltage systems, such as + 12 / 0 / −12 V, + 24 / −24 V.
3) *Equipment Ground Bus.* This is the metallic enclosure, or frame, of the computer equipment. This may include the chassis of the computer elements, as well as the outer enclosure or cabinet. Some computer manufacturers refer to the equipment ground bus as the "Safety Ground Bus."

In addition to the terms listed above for the various ground bus systems, you may encounter such terms as: AC Safety (mains) Grounds, Computer Reference Ground, DC Signal Common, Earth Common, DC Ground Bus, DC Master Ground Point, and Power Supply Common Ground Point. It appears that each computer company has generated its own term for various grounded parts of their systems. There is no uniformity in the terminology, although as you will see later, they all must end up connected together.

5.5 Computer Grounds

5.5.1 Single Point Connection

To prevent stray continuous currents or circulating currents from affecting the computer signals and operation, it is necessary to keep the computer ground system separate from the equipment ground components and connected together *vat only one point*. Actually, it is desirable to keep the computer ground system completely isolated from the electrical power system equipment ground system, except where the two ground systems are connected together, *at only one point*. (See Fig 65.)

The computer manufacturers may have several different ground systems. They may refer to them as the power ground, signal ground, safety ground, etc. With the exception of the safety ground, which usually is the equipment enclosure, required to be grounded by Article 250 of the NEC [1], all the other grounds will usually be terminated on a single point. It is the disposition of this ground point that is the basic cause of concern.

The one point where the two grounding systems, the electrical power grounding system and the computer grounding system, can be connected together is at one of two locations. Figure 70 shows the common point for the electrical power system grounding. The two grounding systems can be connected at this one common grounding point, which should then be the grounding terminal for that assembly. Or the computer grounding system can be connected to the nearest effectively grounded building steel.

Where a computer system master assembly is composed of several enclosures, the internal ground connections, not the enclosure ground, should be routed to one collection point, within the enclosure assemblies, and this one point connected to ground. The collection of the individual grounds should be in the form of a radial distribution system, or a "tree," without any parallel ground paths.

Should the internal signal ground connection be connected to the enclosure instead of insulated from the enclosure, then all the component enclosures need to be insulated from ground or from a conducting floor that they may be supported on. The collective signal/enclosure ground will be connected to the nearest effectively grounded building steel.

If the separate computer-signal ground systems are isolated from the cabinet enclosure and brought together at this one common point, then it is not advisable or necessary to isolate the computer enclosures from the grounded computer floor or from any floor. One computer manufacturer's installation instruction indicated this, calling for insulated plastic conduit coupling. An insulated conduit coupling was a violation of the NEC [1]. In addition, the cooling system or the heating system probably lacked the isolation and negated the isolation effect the manufacture was trying to obtain. (See 5.5.5 for additional information.) For rejection of induced very high frequencies, it may be necessary to have as short a bonding conductor as possible connecting the computer to a ground grid within the floor or to a grounding type computer floor.

5.5.2 Backup Grounds

Occasionally, there is a desire to make grounding electrode-resistance measurements of an electrical installation. This requires the application of voltage between the grounding electrode and one or more external temporary electrodes. The resistance measurement procedure would likely impose over-voltages on any computer system, especially if the computer system has signal lines entering the facility from the outside.

To accommodate the measurement of the ground resistance procedure, it has been found convenient to make a removable connection between the computer grounding terminal and the facility power system grounding electrode and to provide a separate, temporary electrode outside the facility. This temporary reference ground needs to be located outside of, or away from, the influence of the main grounding electrode, to which the grounding connection of the computer is normally connected. The removal of the main ground connection to computer and the connection to the temporary grounding electrode is made only during the time required for testing of the main grounding electrode.

149

The test electrode can be left connected to the computer grounding terminal even after such testing, provided that the original ground connection is connected in parallel, since it is simply a branch of the facility grounding system. (See Reference [5], Chapter 4, p. 130).

5.5.3 Insulated Grounding Conductors

The NEC [1] recognizes that sensitive plug-in equipment such as cash registers, mini-computers, printers, etc. can be adversely affected by currents flowing in common equipment grounding conductors, such as conduit, green or bare ground conductor, building steel, etc. To minimize such problems, the NEC [1], in Section 250-74, Exception No. 4, permits an insulated grounding conductor to be run from the insulated grounding terminal of the receptacle all the way back to the electrical power service grounding point or to the grounded terminal of the insulated grounding terminal of the receptacle all the way back to the electrical power service grounding point or to the grounded terminal of the separately derived system serving the receptacle. This conductor must be run in the wireway, conduit, or raceway, with the conductor serving that receptacle load. This separate conductor is usually green with a yellow stripe. The conductor should not be connected to any grounding buses or common points between the receptacle load and the basic grounding location. This system eliminates much of the noise in plug-connected sensitive electronic equipment. However, problems have arisen because of misinterpretation of Section 250-74, Exception No. 4, and other improper installations.

The use of any insulated grounding conductor and an isolated grounding receptacle does not relieve the requirement for the metal parts of the receptacle box, raceway, conduit, etc. from being connected to the building equipment ground system (see Fig 65). This will usually require the following conductors:

1) Phase Conductor (usually black)
2) Identified (neutral) Conductor (white)
3) System Equipment Ground Conductor (green)
4) Isolated Equipment Ground Conductor (usually green with yellow strip)

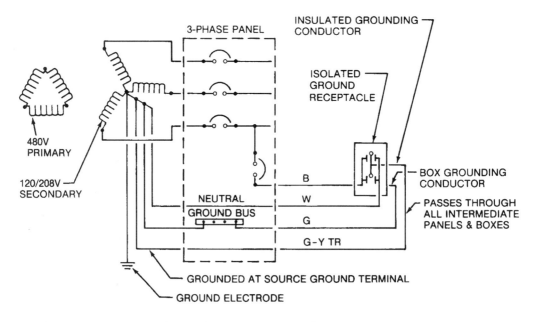

Figure 65—Insulated Grounding Conductor for Sensitive Plug-In Equipment Per NEC [1], Section 250-74, Exception No. 4

Reliance on the metal raceway is not recommended. Harold Kaufmann's tests of where the current flows during a fault on power cables No. 4/0 AWG and larger concluded that an internal grounding conductor improves the efficiency of the ground return path [8]. For conductors No. 12 AWG to No. 6 AWG, Robert West showed that the increase impedance effect is not a factor [9]. Internal ground-return conductors do improve reliability, especially when sensitive electronic equipment grounding is a concern.

Figure 65 illustrates the circuitry and insulated grounding conductor routing through intermediate panel(s) en route to the point where the system is grounded.

Where there are large numbers of these insulated conductors, it is logical to connect them together onto a sensitive grounding bus in the enclosure closest to the grounding electrode and run a large insulated conductor to the main grounding terminal.

5.5.4 Separate/Isolated Grounds

5.5.4.1 Description

Since the power grounding system had been found to be dirty, a logical solution was to not use the building's electrical power equipment grounding system for grounding computers. A possible lack of understanding by manufacturers of the function and operation of the neutral grounding and the ground system led to the following erroneous installation requirements by the sensitive electronic equipment manufacturers. The chosen alternative was to ground computers to an isolated grounding electrode of one or more driven rods separate from the power system grounding electrode system. These generally took the form of one to ten rods a few feet away from the building. These would have grounding resistance of from 10 to 30 Ω or more. This additional resistance usually masked the electrical problem with the computer system by adding the additional impedance into the circuit. The effectiveness of the multiple rods, which were 10 ft (3.05 m) in length, usually driven at a distance of 10 ft apart, was diminished, since the most effective distance between rods is the sum of the depth of the rods. (See 4.1.) This electrical separation of grounding electrodes without bonding all grounding electrodes together did not meet the NEC [1] requirements. Fig 66 shows such a system. In some cases, instead of rods 10 ft in length, multiple rods had been connected together, increasing the length to 20 ft (6.1 m), 30 ft (9.14 m), or more. The length that was used depended on the area of the country, the designer, and/or the contractor.

5.5.4.2 Noise Isolation

The isolated ground system reduces the noise, which had come from the power ground system via multiple grounding connections. In fact, it was called, in some parts of the world, a "quiet ground." Since additional impedance had been injected into the circuit, some noise was still picked up unless all interconnected computers were grounded to the same electrode group. Voltages can exist in the earth between electrodes even a few feet apart; these voltages could be introduced into the different parts of a computer system connected to separate grouping electrodes.

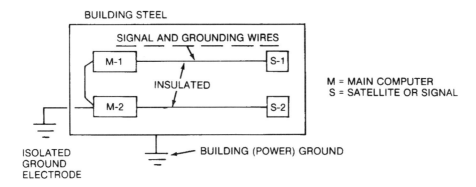

Figure 66—Isolated Grounding of Computers

5.5.4.3 Problems

While continuous low-level noise was eliminated by the isolated ground practice, a number of catastrophic incidents were encountered. Analysis of these indicated that the separation of grounds was responsible for very large voltages being impressed on computer components under thunderstorm conditions. These voltages occurred whether or not computers were in operation. Clearly some change would he necessary. The large voltages were due to lightning striking either the building housing the computers or the power system serving the building. There were other causes that were not so evident. When charge centers on lightning clouds were overhead, charges were induced in buildings on the ground beneath them.

Due to the resistance of the building grounding electrode, the voltage on the building was raised to a substantial level above that of the computers. The computers were held at the voltage of the separated, isolated electrode. This difference in voltage, and the capacitance between computers and building frame, induced voltages into the computer components that were above the breakdown voltages of the components. Many semiconductor components of computers will withstand only about 20 V or less even for as short a time as 1 μs. The described condition is illustrated in Fig 67.

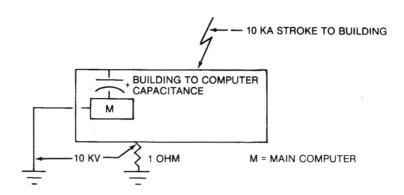

Figure 67—Effects of Stroke to Building with Isolated Grounding Electrode (Not Recommended)

The smaller interfering voltages injected into computer circuitry by the induced voltages of building, due to charges centered in clouds overhead, even without strokes occurring, can cause similar problems. Such induced voltages can cause the absolute voltage of a building to be even a few hundreds of volts different from a grounding system a few tens of feet from the building. These voltages are sporadic and transient and can feed pulses into the computer circuitry, interfering with the desired operation or even causing failure of components.

5.5.4.4 Remote Computer Units

Where remote (satellite) computer units or components are grounded to an isolated grounding electrode at their location, away from the main building, circuit voltage can develop between satellite and main semiconductor devices and destroy them. Fig 68 illustrates this. An isolated repeater usually used with telephone systems, called a "modem," is required to prevent this overvoltage. The modem will make the interconnecting signal wire the equivalent of a telephone circuit. (The word "modem" is a contraction of MOdulator-DEModulator, which is the hardware that connects the data terminal to a communication line.)

5.5.4.5 National Electrical Code Nonadherence

The NEC [1] (Sections 250-5, 26, 51, 54, 57, 58, and 59) requires that all equipment served from an electrical source be grounded or bonded to the grounding point of that source. (In addition, the neutral of all power supplies are required to be grounded, with very few exceptions.) Clearly, when an isolated grounding electrode is used for a computer, this violates the NEC [1] requirements. The NEC [1] requires a metallic path from all equipment frames served, back to the source neutral. If the path has a low impedance, any fault will be of sufficient magnitude to quickly operate the protective device and de-energize the faulted unit. With separate isolated ground electrodes, a fault in a computer requires fault current to pass through the resistance of both the isolated electrode and that of the source building ground, in series. Where the isolated ground electrode resistance is 20 Ω and the building resistance is 20 Ω, a 120 V component fault would cause a current of 120/40 A or 3 A. This amount of current certainly would be insufficient to operate even a 15 A protective device. Fig 69 illustrates this condition.

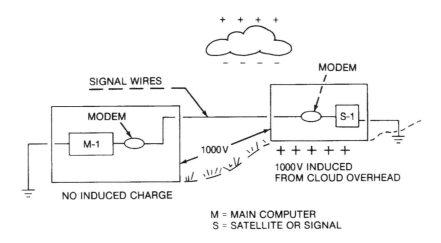

Figure 68—Remote Computer Unit Under a Cloud-Charge Center

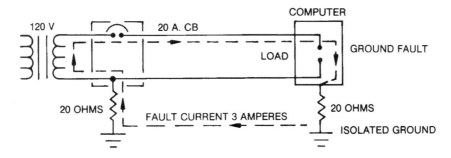

Figure 69—Unsafe Isolated Ground on Computer

Twenty ohms would be a very good resistance value for a single driven ground rod in some parts of the United States. In one computer installation in New Jersey, three separate ground rods were driven in soil near a river bottom. They measured 55, 45, and 30 Ω each. This could be considered typical.

The fault would remain between computer frame and adjacent building metal parts, representing a hazard to personnel. Clearly, this is a condition that must be corrected.

5.5.5 Single Point Grounding System

To eliminate undesirable aspects of previous systems of grounding computers and similar sensitive electronic systems, the Single Point Grounding System has been developed and is the recommended method of grounding sensitive electronic equipment. This overcomes the "noisy" multiple-point power grounding electrode problems, by grounding any one computer system to only one single point on the power grounding system. Any other computers must be grounded to the same single point on the power grounding system as all the rest of the computers. It also overcomes the capacitive induced voltages between building and computer due to separate grounding, by bonding computer and the building to the same electrode.

The resistance of effectively grounded building steel as shown by R. B. West's paper [9], is very low, on the order of less than 1 Ω. When the computer grounding electrode and the electrical power system grounding electrode are connected together, a transient voltage rise applied to the building steel, will result in the entire computer system rising and falling with the building steel. No over-voltage will be induced into the computer circuits.

5.5.6 Central Radial Grounding

Central radial grounding is accomplished by connecting the grounding circuits of the main and satellite units of any one system together, with 600 V insulated wires. This is illustrated in Fig 70. The ground element of the main unit is connected, again with insulated wire, to a single point on the building power system ground. The preferred point is the point at which the "derived power system" or computer supply transformer secondary is grounded. But it *can* be any other single point on the building grounding system or separately derived electrical power system.

Grounding conductors of separate systems of main and satellite units are connected together. (For clarity, referred to as M1.) They are insulated from all other systems (M2) and the building power ground system, except that the main unit ground terminal of each such system is grounded with insulated wire, to one point on the building power ground system. This one point (M1) may be the same point to which other such systems (M2) are grounded, or each system may be a connected to a different point. If a satellite computer system is isolated from the main system with modems adequate to withstand the voltage difference between them, the satellite computer system may be grounded to its own separate ground. This is illustrated in Fig 70.

Computers having signal wiring extending from one building to another building with a separate power supply may be made compatible with the NEC [1] by the use of modems, which permit the separation of grounding connections without introduction of multiple grounding-point noise. These modems are the same devices used for connection of computer signal lines via telephone cables.

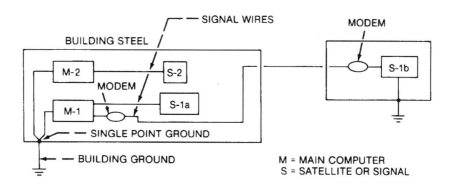

Figure 70—Zero Noise Pickup from Single-Point Grounding of Two-Computer Systems

Where there are several computers in a central location, or "computer room," they may all be grounded to a single point, as shown in Fig 71. They can all conveniently receive their power from a single source, preferably via a local isolating transformer that can be grounded within or at the boundary of the room. This, then, can serve well as the grounding point for all of the computers in that room.

If there is interconnection, those units that are interconnected must share a single signal grounding electrode, a single-point connection to building steel, etc.

Where there are several computer rooms, or computers located at several points within a building, and there is no other connection between the computers, or between the computer rooms, each of these groups or individual units can be grounded to the electrical power ground system (effectively grounded building steel, etc.) at its nearest location.

5.5.7 Local Area Networks

The manufacturers of sensitive electronic equipment and computers recognized the problem of grounding. With advancements in the internal design of computers and the development of Local Area Networks (LANs), the need to be concerned with grounding has all but disappeared. In many LANs systems, the signal wire shield is not connected to the chassis ground but has a common ground. Each computer is plugged into the nearest electrical power receptacle. This design change appears to have reduced the problem; however, there is still the possibility of signal line shield-to-chassis voltage potential during severe ground-fault conditions.

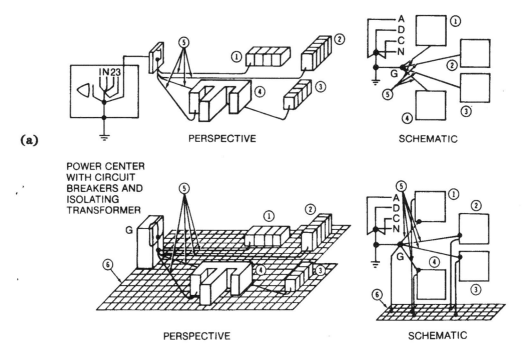

(a)

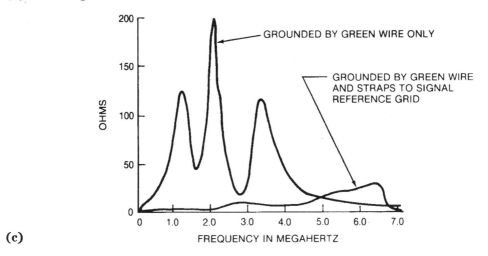

(b)

COMPUTER UNITS CONNECTED TO SIGNAL REFERENCE GRID AND TO A-C GROUND
① THROUGH ④ ARE TYPICAL COMPUTER SYSTEM MODULES.
⑤ IS THE "GREEN WIRE" SAFETY EQUIPMENT GROUND CONDUCTOR.
⑥ IS SAFETY GROUND FOR RAISED FLOOR STRUCTURE.

(c)

Figure 71—Signal Reference Grids Reduce Resonances: (a) Computer Conductors Subject to High-Frequency Resonance with RF Signals, (b) Computer Units Connected to Signal Reference Ground and AC Power Source Ground, (c) Resonance of Power Equipment Ground Conductors in typical Site.

5.5.8 Optical Fibers

In place of the modem in data lines between buildings, per Fig 70, isolation can be obtained by the use of optical fiber lines rather than electric conductors. Some computer manufacturers even provide optical link isolation in input-output terminating lines for this purpose. For entire data lines of optical fiber, it is possible that "repeaters" or amplifiers will be required. Specialists in optical fiber systems, such as the telephone companies, should be consulted. Bear in mind that there are two types of optical systems: long lines, such as those the telephone companies use for long distance transmission; and short lines, which are used for internal building communications and isolation of electrical systems. Each type, long or short, is constructed differently, since each has different applications.

5.6 Effects of Internal Rectifiers in Computers

Most computers, internally, operate on dc obtained from 50-60 Hz ac via rectifiers and filters. The filters, necessary to convert the rectified ac to reasonably pure dc, employ large capacitors and reactors or resistors. The capacitor draws current through the rectifier (and the ac line) only when the rectifier output voltage is above the dc voltage output of the capacitor input of the filter. This is for the short period preceding the peak voltage as shown in Fig 72. This is a peak current well above the 60 Hz sinusoidal current of the computer power supply, and it increases the rms value.

The current pulses in each phase are well above the 50–60 Hz sinusoidal currents and result in a disproportionate increase in the rms current or equivalent heating effect. Due to this high frequency component, the current increase will not register on 50–60 Hz meters. Consequently, the supply conductors may frequently need to be oversized by about one-third even though the current read by 50–60 Hz ammeters will not indicate it. This need for larger line conductors than would normally be required also means that the bus bars in panels and the supply transformers may have to be oversized. (See Fig 73.)

This pulsating current is similar to single phase unbalanced load current. Each pulse when it occurs is a single-phase pulse and is not balanced by the other phases as with three-phase sinusoidal currents offset by 120 degrees Consequently, all pulses are line-to-neutral. The peak currents are high enough that the cumulative rms and heating effect of all three phase pulses may exceed the rms of the line current. Consequently, common neutrals should not be run, and each phase should be equipped with its own neutral.

As stated above, this means that the devices, conductors, and bus bars between the transformer and the start of the single-phase loads will have to be evaluated for overheating.

The distribution and grounding system illustrated in Fig 74 complies with all the requirements of the NEC [1] as well as maintains the isolation and noise rejection required for the computer system. This type of installation is recommended to minimize the numerous incorrect methods of isolated ground installations that violate the safety requirements of the NEC [1] and create hazards to personnel and equipment.

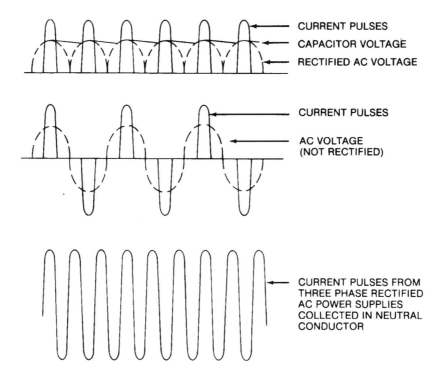

CURRENT PULSES

CAPACITOR VOLTAGE

RECTIFIED AC VOLTAGE

CURRENT PULSES

AC VOLTAGE
(NOT RECTIFIED)

CURRENT PULSES FROM
THREE PHASE RECTIFIED
AC POWER SUPPLIES
COLLECTED IN NEUTRAL
CONDUCTOR

Figure 72—Rectifier Circuit Effect on AC Current

5.7 Grounding of Shields

When rigid metal conduit was used for signal conductors, the metal conduit acted as an overall shield. This overall shield was grounded in multiple locations whenever the metal conduit was fastened to building steel. With the advent of cable tray and other wireway methods, the overall shield has disappeared. Thus, one must consider the need to specify signal conductors with individual shielding and an overall shield when metal conduit is not used. This overall shield will act as the metal conduit shield. The overall shield is grounded whenever and wherever possible for low-frequency applications. The individual shields are grounded according to the applied frequency: low frequency at one end and high frequency at multiple points.

5.7.1 Description/Need

Electrostatic induction into wires carrying low signal voltages has been found to be largely eliminated by installing electrostatic shields around wires. These shields may be:

1) Braided copper wire
2) Metalized foil, with a copper drain wire
3) Metal conduit (if steel conduit, this also serves as a magnetic shield)
4) Other shielding methods

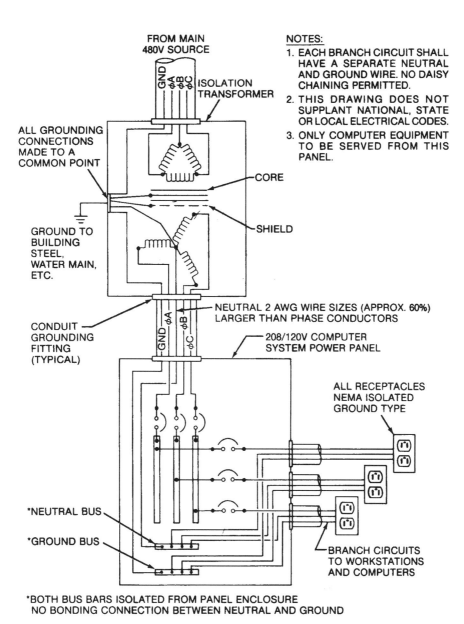

Figure 73—Recommended Power Distribution—Computer System

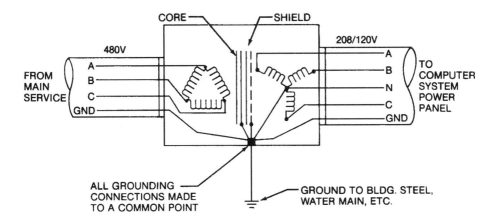

Figure 74—Computer Isolation Transformer

To be effective, shields must be grounded. For signal frequencies of up to about 1 MHz, it is good practice to ground a shield at only one end, preferably at the source of the signal end, leaving the load end insulated from ground. This is to prevent the shield from acting as a conductor for voltage differences at the two ends. This voltage difference may exist between the two different locations on the building steel. When there is current carried in the shield voltage from this current is injected into the signal voltage. This is especially applicable where the signal voltage is between the enclosed conductor and the shield. Where the interfering voltage is low frequency (60 Hz) and the signal is a higher frequency, the insulated end of the shield can be shorted for signal frequency by a suitably sized capacitor. This results in high impedance to the interfering frequency but low impedance to the signal frequency.

As the signal frequency increases above about 1 MHz, it becomes necessary to ground the shield at both ends and possibly even at multiple points between ends. It becomes important that the ground wires be very short; thus, they would be connected to building steel rather than to a circuit grounding point some distance away. A grounding lead develops an impedance proportional to frequency and length. A grounding conductor longer than 1/20, or 0.05%, of the wavelength of the interfering frequency will not properly serve its purpose. Wavelength in meters is 300 divided by the frequency in MHz.

$$\lambda = \frac{300 \cdot 10^6}{f} \tag{9}$$

Where

λ = wavelength (meters per cycle)
f = frequency (cycles per second)
$300 \cdot 10^6$ = constant, velocity of an electromagnetic wave in free space

The speed of an electromagnetic wave in a vacuum is 186 000 miles (300 000 km) per second. The speed is lower in a conductor. A voltage wave will travel approximately 98 ft (29.87 m) in free space during one cycle of a 10-MHz pulse. In a grounding conductor, the wave may travel only 88 ft (26.82 m) in Chapter 1/10 μs. If the conductor is 88 ft long, the wave will be reflected back and arrive at the beginning at the same time that a new pulse begins. Resonance will occur and line oscillations will be greatly magnified.

The peak will occur at 1/4 wavelengths, or in the example of an 88-ft-long conductor, at 22-ft locations. Good engineering practice decrees that a conductor any longer than 1/20 of a wavelength cannot be counted on to equalize voltages between its ends [3].

So for an interfering frequency of 10 MHz, the length may not exceed 1/20, or 0.05%, in 1/10 μs.

$$\frac{0.3048 \text{ ft/m} \cdot 0.05\% \cdot 300.10^6}{10 \cdot 10^6 \text{ MHz}} = 4.5 \text{ ft (1.37 m)} \tag{10}$$

Higher interfering frequencies would require proportionately shorter (inversely) grounding wire lengths, or the shields will be less effective.

5.7.2 Overvoltage at Open Points

At ungrounded ends of shields, some voltage may develop between shield and ground. The shield must be insulated to prevent hazardous personnel exposure. Also, shields must be insulated over their entire length to prevent multiple grounding to points that may be at voltages different from that of the shield and which could inject voltages into the shield.

To terminate the shield, it will be necessary to remove the end of the jacket to reach the shield and open its continuity. The end then must be insulated to prevent possible personnel shock. If shielding must be continued beyond this point, shielding, such as flexible copper-shield braid or expanded shield tubing, needs to be overlapped at the insulated end of the signal shield, spliced to the shield of the continuing length, and grounded at the load end and grounding terminal.

5.8 Interference from Radio Frequencies

Problems from resonance at high frequencies due to length of the grounding conductor from the computer units to the grounding point can be largely eliminated by a grounding grid in the raised floor of the computer room. For each group of computer equipment, a grid network of copper wires in the raised floor, with tie wires from each computer equipment unit to the grid and one from the grid to the room grounding point, will largely negate this resonance effect. Fig 71 illustrates this principle, showing a group without the grid (a) and the same group with the grid (b). A comparison of the performance of the two is shown in (c).

5.9 Case Histories

5.9.1 Corporate Headquarters Office Building Current Flow Over Ground

An office building contained a 1500 kVA lighting transformer in the basement. The computer room was located next to the transformer room. The 102/208 V system had many neutral-to-ground connections, which offered a parallel path for the return current over building steel, piping, etc.

Malfunction of the computer occurred whenever a large load was switched. The total load on the transformer was approximately 1200 A The amount of neutral current returning over the ground ranged from 40 to 60 A.

The multiple computer connections to ground were combined into a single-point connection. Due to the many neutral-to-ground faults, mainly in the lighting fixtures, no attempt was made to correct the situation because of the cost. However, all new construction was checked for neutral-to-ground faults, and the contractor was responsible for finding and making the corrections. In new construction, a typical 42-pole lighting panel was found to contain 20% of the branch circuits faulted with neutral-to-ground faults.

The method for finding neutral-to-ground faults is given in Reference [10].

5.9.2 Corporate Headquarters Office Building Ground Connection

Several large-scale computers in a large corporation headquarters office complex on the 10th floor were each grounded by a grounding conductor in the power-supply cable to the source transformer ground to building steel. The power-supply cable furnished with each computer was a plastic-jacketed type, about 10 ft (3.05 m) long, terminating in a multiconductor plug, with the ground conductor attached to the metal shell of the plug. The user supplied the mating receptacle and cable from the receptacle to the source. This cable was not jacketed but had the ground conductor attached to the cable metal armor.

It was found that separating the cable armor from contact with either the armor of the other cables or (grounded) metal supports for the raised floor reduced the continuous noise level by 90%. Consequently, insulating jackets were applied to the power cables to eliminate the noise interference between separate grounds of the grounding conductors. This also showed that noise was being generated in each computer and that the connection with other computers would introduce noise into all these systems.

5.9.3 U.S. Army Facilities Plant

A computer in a small control building served a number of nearby production facilities. This computer had an isolated ground of 28 Ω resistance to earth and 0.7 Ω resistance separate from the building's power ground system. The computer power supply was from the plant's power system, stabilized by static regulating transformers. In an electrical storm, a pole bearing the transformer servicing the control building, but 300 ft (91.44 m) from it, was struck by lightning. The computer was not in operation, and the main power switches were open. But the computer sustained failure of about one-third of the semiconductor devices in its system. It was apparent that overvoltages did not enter the computer through the power system. The surge arresters on the normal power lines entering the building raised the building-frame voltage substantially. The computer was held by its isolated ground to a lower voltage than that of the building. The capacitance between the computer and the building allowed voltage to be introduced between the two, placing over-voltage on components and causing failure of many of them.

Consequently, the owners interconnected the computer ground conductor with the building's power-system ground. There has been no subsequent mal-function due to lightning. A second production group at the same site was grounded, at a single point, with the building grounding electrode. There were ten computers in this group, interconnected with four remote production buildings. All of these remote terminals were grounded to the central control computers, which were each connected to a heavy ground bus. From that point, a heavy conductor was run to the grounding loop around the building. This loop had a grounding electrode of less than 1 Ω resistance. Trouble-free operation, even though the area where the building was located had a high incidence of lightning, resulted. The computer components in the remote production buildings were insulated from the building ground systems of those buildings.

5.9.4 Restaurant Computer System

A point-of-sale computer system consisting of a central processing unit (CPU) with disk drives and seven remote devices (five terminals and two printers) was installed in a restaurant. The insulated grounds on the branch circuits were connected to isolated ground rods and isolated water pipes. The system was malfunctioning daily.

Shielded, isolated transformers were installed at the CPU and all remote devices. The isolated grounds were bonded to the equipment ground terminals at the subpanels, and all connections to the ground rods and water pipes were removed. Following these changes, the system has operated reliably for over two years.

5.9.5 High Rise Office Building

A computer system consisting of two CPUs, disk drives, tape drives, and several peripherals was installed in an upper floor of a high-rise office building. Power source for the system was a 112.5 kVA transformer located in the electrical room on that floor. The insulated ground from the computer-room panel was installed with the feeder conductors back to the electrical room, where it was terminated at the 500 MCM copper riser for the building.

Both CPUs were experiencing a high incidence of hang-ups, after which the system would have to be power down and restarted. This resulted in the loss of all data.

The connection to the 500 MCM building ground was removed, and the grounding connection made, with the feeder conductors, to the X0 neutral-ground bond of the 112.5 kVA transformer. After this change, the system operated for several months without a single incident of CPU hang-up.

5.9.6 Separate Buildings/Single Ground

Four separate but nearby structures were the control buildings for a series of chemical processes. Each building housed a computer for process control. There were some interconnections between data circuits of the computers and adjoining buildings. Each of the four computers was separately grounded to the structural steel (power) grounding system of its building. Operation of the computer system was completely erratic.

One of the plant engineers suggested that the grounding systems of the four computers be connected together and grounded at only one point: at one of the two center buildings. Erratic operation ceased at once. The NEC [1] was being violated, even though there was a metallic ground-fault return system through the overall plant inter-building bonding system, but of higher impedance.

Interconnection of the computers made the four systems a single system, so grounding at four points induced ground-current loops. Also, at this plant, like all others of that company, all the building frames were interconnected to a single ground system, making them the same as a single building steel combination. So connection to all four would be the same as grounding a system at four points on the same building. Such common grounding can be the result of a metallic water system, shield of ground wires of electric cables, process piping, etc. These can inject such problems into many computer system grounding schemes.

5.10 References

[1] ANSI/NFPA 70-1990, National Electrical Code.[22]

[2] ANSI C2-1990, National Electrical Safety Code. New York: The Institute of Electrical and Electronics Engineers.[23]

[3] FIPS PUB #94, Guideline on Electrical Power for ADP (Automatic Data Processing) Installations, Federal Information Processing Standards Publication, U.S. Department of Commerce, National Bureau of Standards, Sept. 21, 1983.[24]

[4] IEEE Std 100-1988, Dictionary of Electrical and Electronics Terms (ANSI).

[5] IEEE Std 142-1982, Recommended Practice for Grounding of Industrial and Commercial Power Systems (IEEE Green Book) (ANSI).

[6] P1100/Draft 5, Recommended Practice for Powering and Grounding Sensitive Electronic Equipment, June 1992.[25]

[7] Fagan, E. J., and Lee, R. H. "The Use of Concrete-Enclosed Reinforcing Rods as Grounding Electrodes," *IEEE Industry and General Applications* (Now *IEEE Transactions on Industry Applications*), IGA-6, no. 4, July-Aug. 1970, pp 337–347.

---

[22]ANSI/NFPA publications can be obtained from the Sales Department, American National Standards Institute, 1430 Broadway, New York, NY 10018, or from Publication Sales, National Fire Protection Association, Batterymarch Park, Quincy, MA 02269.
[23]IEEE publications are available from the Institute of Electrical and Electronics Engineers, IEEE Service Center, 445 Hoes Lane, Piscataway, N J 08855-1331.
[24]NIST publications are available from the Superintendent of Documents, US Government Printing Office, P.O. Box 37082, Washington, DC 20013-7082, USA.
[25]This authorized standards project was not approved by the IEEE Standards Board at the time this went to press. It is available from the IEEE Service Center.

[8] Kaufmann, R. H. "Some Fundamentals of Equipment Grounding Circuit Design," *IEEE IGA*, vol. 73, part 2, Nov. 1954.

[9] West, R. B. "Equipment Grounding for Reliable Ground Fault Protection in Electrical Systems Below 600 Volts,"*IEEE Transactions on Industry Applications*, vol. 1A-10. no. 2, Mar/Apr. 1974, pp 175–189.

[10] Zipse, D. W. "Multiple Neutral to Ground Connections," presented at IEEE 1972 I&CPS Technical Conference, 72CH0600-7-1A, pp. 60–64.

5.11 Bibliography

Buschart, R. J. Computer Grounding and the National Electrical Code, *IEEE Transactions on Industry Applications*, vol. IA-23, No. 3, May/June 1987 p. 404–407.

Lee, R. H. "Grounding of Computers and Other Similar Sensitive Equipment," *IEEE Transactions on Industry Applications*, vol IA-23, no. 3, May/June 1987, pp. 408–411.

Lewis, W. H. "Recommended Power and Signal Grounding for Control and computer Rooms," *IEEE Transactions on Industry Applications*, vol. IA-21, no. 6, Nov/Dec. 1985, p. 1503.

Lewis, W. H. "The Use and Abuse of Insulated/Isolated Grounding," *IEEE Transactions on Industry Applications*, vol IA-25, no. 6, Nov./Dec. 1989, p. 1093.

Maggioli, V. M. "Grounding and Computer Technology," *IEEE Transactions on Industry Applications*, vol IA-23, no. 3, May/June 1987, pp. 412–417.

"Grounding for Process Control Computers and Distributed Control Systems: The National Electrical Code and Present Grounding Practice," *IEEE Transactions on Industry Applications*, May/June 1987, vol. 1A-23, no. 3 pp. 417–423.